THE CONTINUUM

AND OTHER TYPES OF SERIAL ORDER

WITH AN INTRODUCTION TO CANTOR'S
TRANSFINITE NUMBERS

BY

EDWARD V. HUNTINGTON

ASSOCIATE PROFESSOR OF MATHEMATICS
IN HARVARD UNIVERSITY

SECOND EDITION

DOVER PUBLICATIONS, INC.

PREFACE TO THE SECOND EDITION

THE first edition of this book appeared in 1905 as a reprint from the *Annals of Mathematics*, series 2 (vol. 6, pp. 151–184, and vol. 7, pp. 15–43), under the title: *The Continuum as a Type of Order: an Exposition of the Modern Theory; with an Appendix on the Transfinite Numbers* (The Publication Office of Harvard University, Cambridge, Mass.).

An Esperanto translation by R. Bricard, under the title: *La Kontinuo*, appeared in 1907 (Paris, Gauthier-Villars).

The following reviews (of the original or of the translation) may be noted: by O. Veblen, in *Bull. Amer. Math. Soc.*, vol. 12 (1906), pp. 302–305; by P. E. B. Jourdain, in the *Mathematical Gazette*, vol. 3 (1906), pp. 348–349; by C. Bourlet, in *Nouvelles Annales de Mathématiques*, ser. 4, vol. 7 (1907), pp. 174–176; and by Hans Hahn, in *Monatshefte für Math. u. Physik*, vol. 21 (1910), *Literaturber.*, p. 26. The author is indebted to Professor Veblen and to Professor Hahn for calling his attention to errors in § 62.

The principal modifications in the present edition are the following: § 38 and § 64 have been enlarged; § 62 has been rewritten, and § 62a has been added; the bibliographical notes have been brought more nearly up to date; throughout Chapter VII [formerly called the Appendix (§ 73–§ 91)] the term "normal series" has been replaced by the term "well-ordered series" (for reasons explained in a footnote to § 74); and in § 89a a brief account has been inserted of Hartogs's recent proof of Zermelo's theorem that every class can be well-ordered.

CONTENTS

CHAPTER IV

DENSE SERIES: ESPECIALLY THE TYPE η OF THE RATIONAL NUMBERS

CHAPTER V

CONTINUOUS SERIES: ESPECIALLY THE TYPE θ OF THE REAL NUMBERS

CHAPTER VI

CONTINUOUS SERIES OF MORE THAN ONE DIMENSION, WITH A NOTE ON MULTIPLY ORDERED CLASSES

CHAPTER VII

Well-ordered Series, with an Introduction to Cantor's Transfinite Numbers

THE CONTINUUM
AND OTHER TYPES OF SERIAL ORDER

INTRODUCTION

THE main object of this book is to give a systematic elementary account of the modern theory of the continuum as a type of serial order — a theory which underlies the definition of irrational numbers and makes possible a rigorous treatment of the real number system of algebra.

The mathematical theory of the continuous independent variable, in anything like a rigorous form, may be said to date from the year 1872, when Dedekind's *Stetigkeit und irrationale Zahlen* appeared;* and it reached a certain completion in 1895, when the first part of Cantor's *Beiträge zur Begründung der transfiniten Mengenlehre* was published in the *Mathematische Annalen.*†

While all earlier discussions of continuity had been based more or less consciously on the notions of distance, number, or magnitude, the Dedekind-Cantor theory is based solely on the relation of order. The fact that a complete definition of the continuum has thus been given in terms of order alone has been signalized by Russell ‡ as one

---

* Third (unaltered) edition, 1905; English translation by W. W. Beman, in a volume called Dedekind's *Essays on the Theory of Numbers*, 1901.

† Georg Cantor, *Math. Ann.*, vol. 46 (1895), pp. 481–512; French translation by F. Marotte, in a volume called *Sur les fondements de la théorie des ensembles transfinis*, 1899; English translation by P. E. B. Jourdain, *Contributions to the Founding of the Theory of Transfinite Numbers*, Open Court Publishing Co., 1915. For further references to Cantor's work, see § 74. An interesting contribution to the theory has been made by O. Veblen, *Definitions in terms of order alone in the linear continuum and in well-ordered sets, Trans. Amer. Math. Soc.*, vol. 6 (1905), pp. 165–171.

‡ B. Russell, *Principles of Mathematics*, vol. 1 (1903), p. 303. See also A. N. Whitehead and B. Russell, *Principia Mathematica*, especially vol. 2 (1912) and vol. 3 (1913), where an elaborate account of the theory of order is given in the symbolic notation of modern mathematical logic.

of the notable achievements of modern pure mathematics;* and the simplicity of the ordinal theory, which requires no technical knowledge of mathematics whatever, renders it peculiarly accessible to the increasing number of non-mathematical students of scientific method who wish to keep in touch with recent developments in the logic of mathematics.

The present work has therefore been prepared with the needs of such students, as well as those of the more mathematical reader, in view; the mathematical prerequisites have been reduced (except in one or two illustrative examples) to a knowledge of the natural numbers, 1, 2, 3, . . . , and the simplest facts of elementary geometry; the demonstrations are given in full, the longer or more difficult ones being set in closer type; and in connection with every definition numerous examples are given, to illustrate, in a concrete way, not only the systems which have, but also those which have not, the property in question.

Chapter I is introductory, concerned chiefly with the notion of one-to-one correspondence between two classes or collections. Chapter II introduces simply ordered classes, or series,† and explains the notion of an ordinal correspondence between two series. Chapters III and IV concern the special types of series known as discrete and dense, and chapter V, which is the main part of the book, contains the definition of continuous series. Chapter VI is a supplementary chapter, defining multiply ordered classes, and continuous series in more than one dimension. Chapter VII gives a brief introduction to the theory of the so-called " well-ordered " series, and Cantor's transfinite numbers. An index of all the technical terms is given at the end of the volume.

---

* The fundamental importance of the subject of order may be inferred from the fact that all the concepts required in geometry can be expressed in terms of the concept of order alone; see, for example, O. Veblen, *A system of axioms for geometry, Trans. Amer. Math. Soc.*, vol. 5 (1904), pp. 343–384; or E. V. Huntington, *A set of postulates for abstract geometry, expressed in terms of the simple relation of inclusion, Math. Ann.*, vol. 73 (1913), pp. 522–559.

† The word *series* is here used not in the technical sense of a sum of numerical terms, but in a more general sense explained in § 12.

It will be noticed that while the usual treatment of the continuum in mathematical text-books begins with a discussion of the system of real numbers, the present theory is based solely on a set of postulates the statement of which is entirely independent of numerical concepts (see § 12, § 21, § 41, and § 54). The various number-systems of algebra serve merely as examples of systems which satisfy the postulates — important examples, indeed, but not by any means the only possible ones, as may be seen by inspection of the lists of examples given in each chapter (§§ 19, 28, 51, 63). For the benefit of the non-mathematical reader, I give a detailed explanation of each of the number-systems as it occurs, in so far as the relation of order is concerned (see § 22 for the integers, §51, 3 for the rationals, and §63, 3 for the reals); the operations of addition and multiplication are mentioned only incidentally (see §§ 31, 53, and 65), since they are not relevant to the purely ordinal theory.*

In conclusion, I should say that the bibliographical references throughout the book are not intended to be in any sense exhaustive; for the most part they serve merely to indicate the sources of my own information.

* The reader who is interested in these extra-ordinal aspects of algebra may refer to my paper on *The Fundamental Laws of Addition and Multiplication in Elementary Algebra*, reprinted from the *Annals of Mathematics*, vol. 8 (1906), pp. 1–44 (Publication Office of Harvard University); or to my *Fundamental Propositions of Algebra*, being monograph IV (pp. 149–207) in the volume called *Monographs on Topics of Modern Mathematics relevant to the Elementary Field*, edited by J. W. A. Young (Longmans, Green & Co., 1911). A more elementary treatment may be found in John Wesley Young's *Lectures on Fundamental Concepts of Algebra and Geometry* (Macmillan, 1911).

CHAPTER I

On Classes in General

1. A *class* (*Menge, ensemble*) is said to be determined by any test or condition which every entity (in the universe considered) must either satisfy or not satisfy; any entity which satisfies the condition is said to belong to the class, and is called an *element* of the class.* A *null* or *empty* class corresponds to a condition which is satisfied by no entity in the universe considered.

For example, the class of prime numbers is a class of numbers determined by the condition that every number which belongs to it must have no factors other than itself and 1. Again, the class of men is a class of living beings determined by certain conditions set forth in works on biology. Finally, the class of perfect square numbers which end in 7 is an empty class, since every perfect square number must end in 0, 1, 4, 5, 6, or 9.

2. If two elements a and b of a given class are regarded as interchangeable throughout a given discussion, they are said to be *equal*; otherwise they are said to be *distinct*. The notations commonly used are $a = b$ and $a \neq b$, respectively.

3. A *one-to-one correspondence* between two classes is said to be established when some rule is given whereby each element of one class is paired with one and only one element of the other class, and reciprocally each element of the second class is paired with one and only one element of the first class.

For example, the class of soldiers in an army can be put into one-to-one correspondence with the class of rifles which they carry,

---

* H. Weber, *Algebra*, vol. 1, p. 4. For the sake of uniformity with Peano's *Formulaire de Mathématiques*, I translate *Menge*, or *Mannigfaltigkeit*, by *class* instead of by collection, mass, set, ensemble, or aggregate — all of which terms are in use. For recent discussions of the concept *class*, see the articles cited in § 83.

since (as we suppose) each soldier is the owner of one and only one rifle, and each rifle is the property of one and only one soldier.

Again, the class of natural numbers can be put into one-to-one correspondence with the class of even numbers, since each natural number is half of some particular even number and each even number is double some particular natural number; thus:

$$1, \quad 2, \quad 3, \quad \ldots,$$
$$2, \quad 4, \quad 6, \quad \ldots.^*$$

Again, the class of points on a line AB three inches long can be put into one-to-one correspondence with the class of points on a

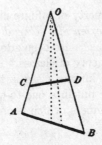

line CD one inch long; for example by means of projecting rays drawn from a point O as in the figure.

4. An example of a relation between two classes which is not a one-to-one correspondence, is furnished by the relation of ownership between the class of soldiers and the class of shoes which they wear; we have here what may be called a two-to-one correspondence between these classes, since each shoe is worn by one and only one soldier, while each soldier wears two and only two shoes. The consideration of this and similar examples shows that all the conditions mentioned in the definition of one-to-one correspondence are essential.

* That the class of square numbers can be put into one-to-one correspondence with the class of all natural numbers was known to Galileo; see his *Dialogs concerning two new Sciences*, translation by Crew and de Salvio (1914), pp. 18–40.

5. Obviously if two classes can be put into one-to-one correspondence with any third class, they can be put into one-to-one correspondence with each other.

6. A *part* ("*proper part*," *echter Teil*), of a class A is any class which contains some but not all of the elements of A, and no other element.

A *subclass* (*Teil*) of A is any class every element of which belongs to A; that is, a subclass is either a part or the whole.

7. We now come to the definition of finite and infinite classes.

An *infinite class* is a class which can be put into one-to-one correspondence with a part of itself. A *finite* class is then defined as any class which is not infinite.

This fundamental property of infinite classes was clearly stated in B. Bolzano's *Paradoxien des Unendlichen* (published posthumously in 1850), and has since been adopted as the definition of infinity in the modern theory of classes.*

8. An example of an infinite class is the class of the natural numbers, since it can be put into one-to-one correspondence with the class of the even numbers, which is only a part of itself (§ 3).

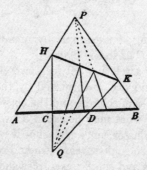

Again, the class of points on a line AB is infinite, since it can be put into one-to-one correspondence with the class of points on a segment CD of AB (by first putting both these classes into one-to-

* See G. Cantor, *Crelle's Journ. für Math.*, vol. 84 (1877), p. 242; and especially R. Dedekind: *Was sind und was sollen die Zahlen*, 1887 (English translation by W. W. Beman, under the title *Essays on the theory of Numbers*, 1901);

one correspondence with the class of points on an auxiliary line HK, as in the figure).

The class of the first n natural numbers, on the other hand, is finite, since if we attempt to set up a correspondence between the whole class and any one of its parts, we shall always find that one or more elements of the whole class will be left over after all the elements of the partial class have been assigned (see § 27).

9. The most important elementary theorems in regard to infinite classes are the following:

(1) *If any subclass of a given class is infinite then the class itself is infinite.*

For, let A be the given class, A' the infinite subclass, and A'' the subclass of all the elements of A which do not belong to A' (noting that A'' may be a null class).

By hypothesis, there is a part, A'_1, of A' which can be put into one-to-one correspondence with the whole of A'; therefore the class composed of A'_1 and A'' will be a part of A which can be put into one-to-one correspondence with the whole of A.

(2) *If any one element is excluded from an infinite class, the remaining class is also infinite.*

For, let A be the given class, x the element to be excluded, and B the class remaining. By hypothesis, there is a part, A_1, of A, which can be put into one-to-one correspondence with the whole of A, and is therefore itself infinite. If this part A_1 does not contain the element x, it will be a subclass in B, and our theorem is proved. If it does contain x, there will be at least one element y which belongs to B and not to A_1, and by replacing x by y in A_1 we shall have another part of A, say A_2, which will be an infinite part of A and at the same time a subclass in B.

10. As a corollary of this last theorem we see that *no infinite class can ever be exhausted by taking away its elements one by one.*

For, the class which remains after each subtraction is always an infinite class, by § 9, 2, and therefore can never be an empty class,

compare B. Russell, *Principles of Mathematics*, vol. 1, p. 315, and Whitehead and Russell, *Principia Mathematica*, vol. 2 (1912), pp. 187–192. See also § 27 of the present paper.

or a class containing merely a single element (these classes being obviously finite according to the definition of § 7).

This result will be used in § 27, below, where another, more familiar, definition of finite and infinite classes will be given.

The further study of the theory of classes as such, leading to the introduction of Cantor's transfinite cardinal numbers, need not concern us here; the definitions of the principal terms which are used in this theory will be found in chapter VII.

11. After the theory of classes, as such, which is logically the simplest branch of mathematics, the next in order of complexity is the theory of classes in which a *relation* or an *operation* among the elements is defined. For example, in the class of numbers we have the relation of " less than " and the operations of addition and multiplication;* in the class of points, the relation of collinearity, etc.; in the class of human beings, the relations " brother of," " debtor of," etc.

If we use the term *system* to denote a class together with any relations or operations which may be defined among its elements we may say that the simplest mathematical systems are:

(1) a class with a single relation, and

(2) a class with a single operation.

The most important example of the first kind is the theory of simply ordered classes, which forms the subject of the present paper; the most important example of the second kind is the theory of abstract groups.† The ordinary algebra of real or complex numbers is a combination of the two.‡

---

* As M. Bôcher has pointed out [*Bull. Amer. Math. Soc.*, vol. 11 (1904), p. 126], any *operation* or *rule of combination* by which two elements determine a third may be interpreted as a triadic relation; for example, instead of saying that two given numbers a and b determine a third number c called their sum $(a + b = c)$, we may say that the three elements a, b, and c satisfy a certain relation $R\ (a, b, c)$.

† For a bibliographical account of the definitions of an abstract group, see *Trans. Amer. Math. Soc.*, vol. 6 (1905), pp. 181–193.

‡ For a definition of ordinary algebra by a set of independent postulates, see *Trans. Amer. Math. Soc.*, vol. 6 (1905), pp. 209–229, or my two monographs cited in the introduction. For a similar definition of the Boolean algebra of

We proceed in the next chapter to explain the conditions or " postulates " which a class, K, and a relation, $<$ (or " R "), must satisfy in order that the system $(K, <)$ may be called a simply ordered class.

logic, see *Trans. Amer. Math. Soc.*, vol. 5 (1904), pp. 288–309 [compare a recent note by B. A. Bernstein, *Bull. Amer. Math. Soc.*, vol. 22 (1916), pp. 458–459]; also papers by H. M. Sheffer, *Trans. Amer. Math. Soc.*, vol. 14 (1913), pp. 481–488, and B. A. Bernstein, *Univ. of California Publications in Math.*, vol. 1 (1914), pp. 87–96, and *Trans. Amer. Math. Soc.*, vol. 17 (1916), pp. 50–52.

CHAPTER II

GENERAL PROPERTIES OF SIMPLY ORDERED CLASSES OR SERIES

12. If a class, K, and a relation, $<$ (called the relation of order), satisfy the conditions expressed in postulates 0, 1–3, below, then the system $(K, <)$ is called a *simply ordered class*, or a *series*.* The notation $a < b$ or $(b > a$, which means the same thing), may be read: " a precedes b " (or " b follows a "). The class K is said to be *arranged*, or *set in order*, by the relation $<$, and the relation $<$ is called a *serial relation* within the class K.

POSTULATE 0. *The class K is not an empty class, nor a class containing merely a single element.*

This postulate is intended to exclude obviously trivial cases, and will be assumed without further mention throughout the paper.

POSTULATE 1. *If a and b are distinct elements of K, then either $a < b$ or $b < a$.*†

POSTULATE 2. *If $a < b$, then a and b are distinct.*‡

POSTULATE 3. *If $a < b$ and $b < c$, then $a < c$.*§

The consistency and independence of these postulates will be established in § 19 and § 20.

13. As an immediate consequence of postulates 2 and 3, we have

Theorem I. If $a < b$ is true, then $b < a$ is false.‖

---

* " *Einfach geordnete Menge:* " G. Cantor, *Math. Ann.*, vol. 46 (1895), p. 496; " *series:* " B. Russell, *Principles of Mathematics*, vol. 1 (1903), p. 199.

† This postulate 1 has been called by Russell the postulate of *connexity*; *loc. cit.*, p. 239.

‡ Any relation $<$ which satisfies postulate 2 is said to be *irreflexive* throughout the class; this term is due to Peano; see Russell, *loc. cit.*, p. 219.

§ Any relation $<$ which satisfies postulate 3 is said to be *transitive* throughout the class. This term has been in common use since the time of DeMorgan.

‖ Any relation $<$ which has this property is said to be *asymmetrical* throughout the class; see Russell, *loc. cit.*, p. 218.

(For, if $a < b$ and $b < a$ were both true, we should have, by 3, $a < a$, whence, by 2, $a \neq a$, which is absurd).

If desired, this theorem I may be used in place of postulate 2 in the definition of a serial relation.

14. The general properties of series may now be summarized as follows:

If a and b are any elements of K, then either

$$a = b, \text{ or } a < b, \text{ or } b < a,$$

and these three conditions are mutually exclusive; further, if $a < b$ and $b < c$, then $a < c$.

These are the properties which characterize a serial relation within the class K.*

15. As the most familiar examples of series we mention the following: (1) the class of all the natural numbers (or the first n of them), arranged in the usual order; and (2) the class of all the points on a line, the relation " $a < b$ " signifying " a on the left of b." Many other examples will occur in the course of our work.

16. If two series can be brought into one-to-one correspondence in such a way that the order of any two elements in one is the same as the order of the corresponding elements in the other, then the two series are said to be *ordinally similar*, or to belong to the same *type of order (Ordnungstypus)*.†

For example, the class of all the natural numbers, arranged in the usual order, is ordinally similar to the class of all the even numbers, arranged in the usual order (compare § 3).

Again, the class of all the points on a line one inch long, arranged from left to right, is ordinally similar to the class of all the points on a line three inches long, arranged from left to right (compare § 8).

---

* A serial relation may also be described as one which is (1′) connected; (2′) irreflexive; (3′) transitive for distinct elements; and (4′) asymmetrical for distinct elements; these four properties [(3′) and (4′) being weaker forms of postulate 3 and theorem I respectively] are readily shown to be *independent*. See a forthcoming paper by E. V. Huntington cited in § 20, below.

† Cantor, *Math. Ann.*, vol. 46 (1895), p. 497.

It will be noticed that in the first of these examples the correspondence between the two series can be set up in only one way, while in the second example, the correspondence can be set up in an infinite number of ways. This distinction is an important one, for which, unfortunately, no satisfactory terminology has yet been proposed.*

17. Before giving further examples of the various types of simply ordered classes, it will be convenient to give here the definitions of a few useful technical terms.

DEFINITION 1. In any series, if $a < x$ and $x < b$, then x is said to lie *between* a and b.†

DEFINITION 2. In any series, if $a < x$ and no element exists between a and x, then x is called the element *next following a*, or the (immediate) *successor* of a. Similarly, if $y < a$ and no element exists between y and a, then y is called the element *next preceding a*, or the (immediate) *predecessor* of a.‡

For example, in the class of natural numbers in the usual order every element has a successor, and every element except the first has a predecessor; but in the class of points on a line, in the usual order, every two points have other points between them, so that no point has either a successor or a predecessor.

DEFINITION 3. In any series, if one element x precedes all the other elements, then this x is called the *first* element of the series. Similarly, if one element y follows all the others, then this y is called the *last* element.

18. With regard to the existence of first and last elements, all series may be divided into four groups: (1) those that have neither a first element nor a last element; (2) those that have a first element, but no last; (3) those that have a last element, but no first; and (4) those that have both a first and a last.

---

* Cf. *Trans. Amer. Math. Soc.*, vol. 6 (1905), p. 41; or O. Veblen, *Bull. Amer. Math. Soc.*, vol. 12 (1906), p. 303. One might speak of a determinate correspondence and an indeterminate correspondence (Bricard).

† For an elaborate analysis of this concept, see a forthcoming paper called "Sets of independent postulates for betweenness," by E. V. Huntington and J. R. Kline, *Trans. Amer. Math. Soc.*

‡ See footnote † under § 31.

For example, the class of all the points on a line *between* A and B, arranged from A to B, has no first point, 1) A —————— B and no last point, since if any point C of 2) A •———— B the class be chosen there will be points of 3) A ————• B the class between C and A and also be- 4) A •————• B tween C and B. If, however, we consider a new class, comprising all the points between A and B, *and also* the point A (or B, or both), arranged from A to B, then this new class will have a first element (or a last element, or both). The four cases are represented in the accompanying diagram.

Examples of series

19. In this section we give some miscellaneous examples of simply ordered classes, to illustrate some of the more important types of serial order. Most of these examples will be discussed at length in later chapters.

In each case a class K and a relation $\prec$ are so defined that the system $(K, \prec)$ satisfies the conditions expressed in postulates 1–3 (§ 12). The existence of any one of these systems is sufficient to show that the postulates are *consistent*, that is, that no two contradictory propositions can be deduced from them. For, the postulates and all their logical consequences express properties of these systems, and no really existent system can have contradictory properties.*

(1) $K =$ the class of all the natural numbers (or the first n of them), with $\prec$ defined as " less than."

This is an example of a " discrete series " (see chapter III).

(2) $K =$ the class of all the points on a line (with or without end-points), with $\prec$ defined as " on the left of."

This is an example of a " continuous series " (see chapter V).

---

* On the consistency of a set of postulates, see a problem of D. Hilbert's, translated in *Bull. Amer. Math. Soc.*, vol. 8 (1902), p. 447, and a paper by A. Padoa, *L'Enseignement Mathématique*, vol. 5 (1903), pp. 85–91. Also D. Hilbert, *Verhandl. des. 3. internat. Math.-Kongresses in Heidelberg*, 1904, pp. 174–185; French translation, *Ens. Math.*, vol. 7 (1905), pp. 89–103; English translation, *Monist*, vol. 15 (1905), pp. 338–352.

(3) K = the class of all the points on a square (with or without the points on the boundary), with < defined as follows: let x and y represent the distances of any point of the square from two adjacent sides; then of two points which have unequal x's, the one having the smaller x shall precede, and of two points which have the same x, the one having the smaller y shall precede. In this way all the points of the square are arranged as a simply ordered class.

(4) By a similar device, the points of all space can be arranged as a simply ordered class. Thus, let x, y, and z be the distances of any point from three fixed planes; then in each of the eight octants into which all space is divided by the three planes, arrange the points in order of magnitude of the x's, or in case of equal x's, in order of magnitude of the y's, or in case of equal x's and equal y's, in order of magnitude of the z's; and finally arrange the octants themselves in order from 1 up to 8, paying proper attention to the points on the bounding planes.

(5) K = the class of all proper fractions, arranged in the usual order.

This is an example of a series called " denumerable and dense " (see chapter IV).

By a *proper fraction* (written m/n) we mean an ordered pair of natural numbers, of which the first number, m, called the numerator, and the second number, n, called the denominator, are relatively prime, and m is less than n; and by the " usual order " we mean that a fraction m/n is to precede another fraction p/q whenever the product $m \times q$ is less than the product $n \times p$. The class as so ordered clearly satisfies the conditions 1–3, as one sees by a moment's calculation.

(6) K = the class of all proper fractions arranged in a special order, as follows: of two fractions which have unequal denominators, the one having the smaller denominator shall precede, and of two fractions which have the same denominator the one having the smaller numerator shall precede.

In contrast with example (5), this series is of the same type as the series of the natural numbers arranged in the usual order, as the following correspondence will show (compare § 42):*

* Cf. G. Cantor, *loc. cit.* (1895), p. 496.

1	2	3	4	5	6	7	8	9	10	11	$\cdots$
$\frac{1}{2}$	$\frac{1}{3}$	$\frac{2}{3}$	$\frac{1}{4}$	$\frac{3}{4}$	$\frac{1}{5}$	$\frac{2}{5}$	$\frac{3}{5}$	$\frac{4}{5}$	$\frac{1}{6}$	$\frac{5}{6}$	$\cdots\cdots$

These two examples, (5) and (6), illustrate the obvious fact that the same class may be capable of being arranged in various different orders.

(7) As another example, let K be a class whose elements are natural numbers affected with other natural numbers as subscripts; for example, 1_1, 5_4, etc.; and let the relation of order be defined as follows: of two numbers which have unequal subscripts, the one having the smaller subscript shall precede, and of two numbers which have the same subscript, the smaller number shall precede. The system may be represented thus, the relation $<$ being read as " on the left of: "

$$1_1, 2_1, 3_1, \ldots; \ 1_2, 2_2, 3_2, \ldots; \ 1_3, 2_3, 3_3, \ldots; \ldots$$

This is an example of what Cantor has called, in a technical sense, a " well-ordered series " (see chapter VII).

(8) An example of a somewhat different character is the following: * let K be the class of all possible infinite classes of the natural numbers, no number being repeated in any one class; † and let these classes be arranged, or set in order, as follows: any class a shall precede another class b when the smallest number in a is less than the smallest number in b, or, if the smallest n numbers of a and b are the same, when the $(n + 1)$st number of a is less than the $(n + 1)$st number of b.

A moment's reflection shows that this system satisfies the conditions for an ordered class; it will appear later that it belongs to the type of series called continuous (see § 63, 5).

A more familiar example of the same type is the following:

(9) $K =$ the class of all non-terminating decimal fractions between 0 and 1, arranged in the usual order. (Compare § 40.)

* B. Russell, *Principles of Mathematics*, vol. 1, p. 299.

† For example, the class of all prime numbers, or the class of all even numbers, or the class of all even numbers greater than 1000, or the class of all perfect cube numbers, or the class of all numbers that begin with 9, or the class of all numbers that do not contain the digit 5, would be an element of K.

By a *non-terminating decimal fraction* between 0 and 1, we mean a rule or agreement by which every natural number has assigned to it some one of the ten digits 0, 1, 2, . . . , 9, excluding, however, the rules which would assign a 0 to every number after any given number (these excluded rules giving rise to the *terminating* decimals).* The digit assigned to any particular number n is called the nth digit of the decimal, or the digit in the nth place. By the " usual order " within this class, we mean that any decimal a is to precede another decimal b when the first digit of a is less than the first digit of b, or, if the first n digits of a and b are the same, when the $(n + 1)$st digit of a is less than the $(n + 1)$st digit of b (the digits being taken in the order of magnitude from 0 to 9).

All these examples of simply ordered classes have been chosen from the domains of arithmetic and geometry; among the other examples which readily suggest themselves the following may be mentioned:

(10) The class of all instants of time, arranged in order of priority.

(11) The class of all one's distinct sensations, of any particular kind, as of pleasure, pain, color, warmth, sound, etc., arranged in order of intensity.

(12) The class of all events in any causal chain, arranged in order of cause and effect.

(13) The class of all moral or commercial values, arranged in order of superiority.

(14) The class of all measurable magnitudes of any particular kind, as lengths, weights, volumes, etc., arranged in order of size.

Examples of systems $(K, <)$ which are not series

20. In this section we give some examples of systems $(K, <)$ which are not series because they satisfy only two of the three conditions expressed in postulates 1–3 (§ 12). The existence of these systems proves that the three postulates are independent — that is, that no one of them can be deduced from the other two. (For,

---

* It should be noticed that what we are here required to grasp is not the infinite totality of digits in the decimal fraction, but simply the rule by which those digits are determined.

if any one of the three properties were a logical consequence of the other two, every system which had the first two properties would have the third property also, which, as these examples show, is not the case.) In other words, no one of the three postulates is a redundant part of the definition of a serial relation.*

(1) *Systems not satisfying postulate* 1 (namely: if $a \neq b$, then $a < b$ or $b < a$).

(*a*) Let K be the class of all natural numbers, with $<$ so defined that a precedes b when and only when $2a$ is less than b.

(*b*) Let K be the class of all human beings, throughout history, with $<$ defined as " ancestor of."

(*c*) Let K be the class of all points (x, y) in a given square, with $(x_1, y_1) < (x_2, y_2)$ when and only when x_1 is less than x_2 and y_1 less than y_2.

In all these systems, postulates 2 and 3 are clearly satisfied.†

(2) *Systems not satisfying postulate* 2 (namely: if $a < b$, then $a \neq b$).

(*a*) Let K be the class of all natural numbers with $a < b$ signifying " a less than or equal to b."

(*b*) Let K be any class, with $a < b$ signifying " a is co-existent with b."

Both these systems satisfy postulates 1 and 3.

(3) *Systems not satisfying postulate* 3 (namely: if $a < b$ and $b < c$, then $a < c$).

(*a*) Let K be the class of all natural numbers, with $<$ meaning " different from."

---

* This method of proving the independence of a set of postulates is the method which has been made familiar in recent years by the work of Peano (1889), Padoa, Pieri, and Hilbert (1899). For a discussion of the " complete independence " of these postulates in the sense defined by E. H. Moore (1910), see a forthcoming paper by E. V. Huntington, *Complete existential theory of the postulates for serial order, Bull. Amer. Math. Soc.* (1917).

† Another very interesting example of a system of this kind is the so-called " conical order " studied by A. A. Robb in his book: *A Theory of Time and Space* (Cambridge, Eng., 1914).

(b) Let K be a class of any odd number of points distributed at equal distances around the circumference of a circle, with $a < b$ meaning that the arc from a to b, in the counter-clockwise direction of rotation, is less than a semi-circle.

(c) Let K be a family of brothers, with $a < b$ signifying " a is a brother of b." This relation is not transitive, since from $a < b$ and $b < a$ it does not follow that $a < a$.

All three of these systems clearly satisfy postulates 1 and 2.

In the following chapters we consider in detail those types of series which are especially important in the study of algebra.

CHAPTER III

DISCRETE SERIES: ESPECIALLY THE TYPE ω OF THE NATURAL NUMBERS

21. A *discrete series* may be defined as any series $(K, \prec)$ which satisfies not only the general conditions 1–3 of § 12, but also the special conditions expressed in postulates $N1$–$N3$, below:

POSTULATE $N1$. (*Dedekind's postulate.**) *If K_1 and K_2 are any two non-empty parts of K, such that every element of K belongs either to K_1 or to K_2 and every element of K_1 precedes every element of K_2, then there is at least one element X in K such that:*

(1) *any element that precedes X belongs to K_1, and*

(2) *any element that follows X belongs to K_2.*

The significance of this postulate $N1$ will be best explained by the examples, given below, of series which have and those which do not have the property in question. For the present it is sufficient to remark that whenever the postulate is satisfied, K_1 will have a last element, or K_2 will have a first element, or both; whichever one of these elements exists (or either of them if they both exist) will serve as the element X required, and may be said to "divide" the two parts K_1 and K_2.

POSTULATE $N2$. *Every element of K, unless it be the last, has an immediate successor* (§ 17).

POSTULATE $N3$. *Every element of K, unless it be the first, has an immediate predecessor* (§ 17).

The consistency and independence of these postulates are shown in §§ 28–29.

---

* R. Dedekind, *Stetigkeit und irrationale Zahlen*, 1872; cf. § 62, below. The selection of postulates here given for discrete series is the same as that adopted by O. Veblen, *Trans. Amer. Math. Soc.*, vol. 6 (1905), pp. 165–171. As far as I know, Dedekind's postulate had not been used by earlier writers in this connection.

22. An example of a discrete series is the class of all integers (positive, negative, and zero), arranged in the usual order:

$$\ldots, \ ^{-}3, \ ^{-}2, \ ^{-}1, \quad 0, \quad ^{+}1, \ ^{+}2, \ ^{+}3, \ldots.$$

The elements of this system are of three kinds: (1) the positive integers, which are natural numbers affected with the sign $+$; (2) the negative integers, which are natural numbers affected with the sign $-$; and (3) an extra element called zero. The " usual order " is more precisely defined as follows: of two positive integers, the one that is numerically smaller precedes; of two negative integers, the one that is numerically greater precedes; every negative integer precedes and every positive integer follows the integer zero; and of two integers of opposite signs, the negative precedes the positive.

By making this series terminate in one or both directions we have an example of a discrete series with a first element or a last element or both. (For another example, see § 28.).

23. The most important property of discrete series is expressed in the often cited " theorem of mathematical induction," which may be stated in the following form:

Theorem of mathematical induction. If a and b are any two elements of a discrete series, and $a < b$, then: if we start from a and form the sequence of elements $p_1, p_2, p_3, \ldots$, in which p_1 is the successor of a, p_2 the successor of p_1, and so on, *some one of these p's will be the element b;* or again, if we start from b and form the sequence $q_1, q_2, q_3, \ldots$, in which q_1 is the predecessor of b, q_2 the predecessor of q_1, and so on, *some one of these q's will be the element a.*

In other words, the class of elements between any two elements of a discrete series can be exhausted by taking away its elements one by one, and is therefore a finite class (by § 10).

The significance of this theorem will be clearer after a study of the examples in § 29 of series in which the theorem does not hold. The formal proof from postulates 1–3 and $N1$–$N3$ is as follows:

Suppose, in the first case considered in the theorem, that the sequence $a, p_1, p_2, p_3, \ldots$ (which we shall call the sequence P) did *not* contain the element b. On this supposition, b would come after all the elements of P, and we could divide the whole series K into two non-empty parts, namely: K_1, containing every element which is equalled or surpassed by any element of P; and K_2, containing every element which (like the element b) comes after all the elements of P. Then by Dedekind's postulate there would be an element X " dividing " K_1 from K_2 so that the predecessor of X would belong to P while the successor of X would not. But this is impossible, since, by the way in which the sequence P is constructed, if the predecessor of X belonged to P, then X itself, and hence the successor of X, would also belong to P. Thus the supposition with which we started has led to contradiction, and the first half of the theorem is proved.

The second half is proved in a similar way.

All discrete series may be divided into four groups, distinguished by the presence or absence of extreme elements; we consider the four cases separately, as follows:

1. *Progressions: series of the type " ω."*

24. A discrete series (§ 21) which has a first element, but no last, is called a *progression.**

All progressions are ordinally similar, that is, any two of them can be brought into one-to-one correspondence in a way that preserves the relations of order.

For, we can assign the first element of one of the progressions to the first element of the other, the successor of that element in one to the successor of that element in the other, and so on; and by the theorem of mathematical induction no element of either series will be inaccessible to this process.

We may therefore speak of the progressions as constituting a definite type of order, which Cantor † has called the *type ω*. Moreover, the ordinal correspondence between two progressions can be set up in *only one way;* this fact will be useful to us later (see § 31).

The simplest example of a progression is the series of natural numbers in the usual order:

$$1, \quad 2, \quad 3, \quad \ldots$$

Other examples are: the even numbers, or the prime numbers, or the perfect square numbers, in the usual order; or the proper fractions arranged in the special order described in § 19, 6.

---

* B. Russell, *Principles of Mathematics*, vol. 1, p. 239.

† G. Cantor, *Math. Ann.*, vol. 46 (1895), p. 499.

2. *Regressions: series of the type " *ω."*

25. A discrete series (§ 21) which has a last element but no first is called a *regression*.

The regressions, like the progressions, constitute a definite type of order, which Cantor has called the *type* *ω (read: star omega). The simplest example of a regression is the series of negative integers with or without zero, arranged in the usual order, thus:

$$. . . , \ ^-3, \ ^-2, \ ^-1, \ 0.$$

3. *Series of the type " *ω + ω."*

26. A discrete series (§ 21) which has neither a first nor a last element may be called an *unlimited discrete series*, the simplest example being the series of all integers in the usual order (§ 22).

In any unlimited discrete series, if any element is chosen as an " origin," the elements preceding this element form a regression and those following it a progression; hence all unlimited discrete series are ordinally similar, and constitute a third definite type of order. Cantor denotes this type by *ω + ω, the plus sign being used to indicate that a series of the type *ω is to be followed by a series of the type ω, and the whole regarded as a single series.

It should be noticed that the correspondence between two series of the type *ω + ω can be set up in an infinite number of ways, since any element may be taken as the origin; compare the following scheme:

$$. . . , \ ^-4, \ ^-3, \ ^-2, \ ^-1, \ \ 0, \ ^+1, \ ^+2, \ ^+3, \ ^+4, \ . . .$$
$$. . . , \ ^-2, \ ^-1, \ \ 0, \ ^+1, \ ^+2, \ ^+3, \ ^+4, \ ^+5, \ ^+6, \ . . . .$$

4. *Finite series*

27. A discrete series (§ 21) which has a first element and a last element will be simply a *finite series*, the word finite being used in the sense defined in § 7.

For, by the theorem of mathematical induction (§ 23), the class of elements in such a series can be exhausted by taking the elements away one by one; therefore, by § 10, it cannot be an infinite class.

And conversely, *every finite class can be put into one-to-one correspondence with a terminated portion of a discrete series.*

These theorems may be used, if one prefers, as the definition of a finite class (compare § 7); an infinite class would then be defined as one which is not finite.

Other examples of discrete series

28. The examples of a discrete series so far mentioned have all been drawn from the domain of arithmetic (as the series of all integers, the series of all positive integers, the series of all negative integers, and series containing only a finite number of elements). The existence of any one of these systems is sufficient to establish the *consistency* of the postulates of this chapter (compare § 19). In this section we give a non-numerical example, due essentially to Dedekind, and phrased in its present form by Royce: *

Suppose a complete map of London could be laid out on the pavement of one of the squares of the city; then the city of London would be represented an infinite number of times in this map, and the successive representations would form a progression. For the map itself would form a part of the object which it represents, and would therefore include a miniature representation of itself; this representation being again a complete map of the city would contain a still smaller representation of itself; and so on, *ad infinitum.*†

Examples of series which are not discrete

29. In this section we give some examples of series (§ 12) which are not discrete (§ 21), each example being a series $(K, \prec)$ which satisfies two of the postulates $N1$–$N3$ but not the third. The existence of these systems proves (see § 20) that the postulates $N1$–$N3$ are independent, that is, that no one of them is redundant in the definition of a discrete series.

---

* R. Dedekind, *Was sind und was sollen die Zahlen*, 1887; J. Royce, *The World and the Individual*, vol. 1, 1900, p. 503.

† Another example of such a *self-representative system* is a label on a can of baking-powder, containing a picture of the can. Another example is provided by the images observed in a pair of parallel mirrors.

(1) *A system not satisfying N1* (Dedekind's postulate). Let K consist of two sets of integers — call them red and blue — the integers of each set being positive, negative, or zero; and let the elements be arranged along a line from left to right, as follows:

red	blue
..., $^-2$, $^-1$, 0, $+1$, $+2$, ...	..., $^-2$, $^-1$, 0, $+1$, $+2$, ...

This system is a series in which every element has a successor, and every element has a predecessor; but Dedekind's postulate, although it holds in general, fails in case K_1 contains all the red elements and K_2 all the blue.

By leaving out the negative integers in the red set, or the positive integers in the blue set, or both, we can readily construct a series of the same sort having either or both extreme elements; the series as it stands has neither.

(2) *A system not satisfying N2* (on successors). Let K consist of a set of negative integers (in red), followed by a set of all integers (in blue), arranged in the usual order, as indicated here:

red	blue
..., $^-3$, $^-2$, $^-1$,	... $^-2$, $^-1$, 0, $+1$, $+2$, $+3$, ...

In this series every element has a predecessor, and Dedekind's postulate is satisfied in all cases; but the element $^-1$ of the red set has no immediate successor.

Systems of the same sort, with one or both extreme elements, can be at once derived.

(3) *A system not satisfying N3* (on predecessors). Similarly, let K consist of a set of all integers (in red), followed by a set of positive integers (in blue), arranged as follows:

red	blue
..., $^-2$, $^-1$, 0, $+1$, $+2$, ...	$+1$, $+2$, $+3$, ...

The theorem of mathematical induction is false in all these systems, since we cannot pass from a red element to a blue element by a finite number of steps.

Examples of series which satisfy *none* of the postulates $N1$–$N3$ will occur in the following chapter (§ 51).

Numbering the elements of a discrete series

30. By " numbering " the elements of a discrete series, we mean simply attaching to each element some label or tag, by which it can be permanently recognized, and distinguished from any other element.

If the given series has a first element or a last element (or both), this may be accomplished as follows, by the use of ten characters called *digits*, 1, 2, 3, 4, 5, 6, 7, 8, 9, 0.

In the case of a progression, denote the first element by 1; the successor of 1 by 2; the successor of 2 by 3; and so on, until the successor of 8 is denoted by 9. Then denote the successor of 9 by 10 (read " one, zero "); the successor of 10 by 11 (read " one, one "); the successor of 11 by 12; and so on, until the successor of 18 is denoted by 19. Then denote the successor of 19 by 20; the successor of 20 by 21; and so on, the successor of 99 being denoted by 100, etc.:

$$1, \ 2, \ 3, \ \ldots \ .$$

By carrying the process far enough *any given element* of the progression can be reached, in virtue of the theorem of mathematical induction.

In the case of a regression, we can number the elements in a similar way, if we begin with the last element and run backward. In this case it is customary to attach the sign $^-$ to each label, the last element of the series being denoted by $^-1$, the predecessor of $^-1$ by $^-2$, the predecessor of $^-2$ by $^-3$, and so on:

$$\ldots, \ ^-3, \ ^-2, \ ^-1.$$

In the case of a finite discrete series, the elements may be numbered in either way, forward or backward:

$$1, \quad 2, \quad 3, \quad 4, \quad 5,$$
$$^-5, \ ^-4, \ ^-3, \ ^-2, \ ^-1.$$

If, however, the given series is unlimited (§ 26), there is no element which we can take as an absolute starting point, since no element is distinguished from the rest by any *ordinal* property. The best we can do in this case is to choose arbitrarily some element

as an origin, denoted by 0, and then number the elements following
0 as a progression, and the elements preceding 0 as a regression; in
this way each element has attached to it a label which indicates its
position in the series, not absolutely, but with reference to the
arbitrarily chosen origin:

$$. . . , \ ^{-}3, \ ^{-}2, \ ^{-}1, \ \ 0, \ ^{+}1, \ ^{+}2, \ ^{+}3, \ . \ . \ . \ .$$

It should be noticed in all these cases that the process of labelling
the elements does not involve the notion of " counting " in the
sense of ascertaining " how many "; the combination of digits
attached to each element is simply a tag by which it can be recognized, like the numbers in a telephone book; when any two
elements thus labelled are given, we can determine at once which
precedes the other in the series without concerning ourselves at all
with the question " how many " elements may lie between them.*

*Digression on sums and products of the elements of a
discrete series*

31. The same principle of mathematical induction which made
it possible to " number " each element of a discrete series (§ 30),
makes it possible to define the sum and the product of any two
elements of such a series in terms of the relation of order.† If the

* Instead of the decimal system of numeration here described we can use
also the less familiar, but often more convenient, binary system, in which only
two digits are required. Thus, in the binary system the successive elements of
a progression would be denoted by: 1; 10, 11; 100, 101, 110, 111; 1000, 1001,
1010, 1011, 1100, 1101, 1110, 1111; 10000, etc. (The digits are read separately:
101 = " one, zero, one," etc.) The advantage of any such system of numeration over the primitive system of strokes (/, //, ///, ////, etc.) lies in the fact
that each digit acquires a special value by virtue of the *place* which it occupies in
the symbol.

† The following sections (§§ 32–35) are due essentially to Peano (1889),
although Peano's postulates for a progression are based not on the notion of
order, but on the notion of " successor of." The postulates adopted in the
present paper seem to me preferable in several respects to those employed by
Peano, especially in the use of Dedekind's postulate in place of the more obvious
postulate of mathematical induction (cf. footnote under § 21). A brief
account of Peano's postulates will be found in *Bull. Amer. Math. Soc.*, vol. 9

series has a first element or a last element (or both), the sums and products are defined absolutely; if the series is unlimited, the sums and products are defined with reference to an arbitrarily chosen origin.

32. We begin with the general case of an unlimited discrete series, and suppose that an origin has been chosen and the elements labelled as in the preceding section:

$$\ldots, \; {}^-3, \; {}^-2, \; {}^-1, \; 0, \; {}^+1, \; {}^+2, \; {}^+3, \; \ldots\ldots$$

The *sum*, $a + b$ of two elements a and b, with respect to the origin 0, is then defined as follows:

(1) $a + 0 = a$ and $0 + a = a$.

(2) $a + {}^+1 =$ the successor of a; $a + {}^+2 =$ the successor of $a + {}^+1$; $a + {}^+3 =$ the successor of $a + {}^+2$; and so on; in general,

$a +$ (the successor of ${}^+n$) = the successor of $(a + {}^+n)$.

(3) $a + {}^-1 =$ the predecessor of a; $a + {}^-2 =$ the predecessor of $a + {}^-1$; $a + {}^-3 =$ the predecessor of $a + {}^-2$; and so on; in general,

$a +$ (the predecessor of ${}^-n$) = the predecessor of $(a + {}^-n)$.

In this way the sum of any two elements can be determined, by virtue of the theorem of mathematical induction (§ 23).

On the basis of this definition of the sum, the *product $a \times b$* (or $a \cdot b$, or ab) of a and b, with respect to the origin 0, is defined as follows:

(1) $0 \times a = 0$ and $a \times 0 = 0$.

(2) ${}^+1 \times a = a$; ${}^+2 \times a = ({}^+1a) + a$; ${}^+3 \times a = ({}^+2a) + a$; and so on; in general (the successor of ${}^+n) \times a = ({}^+na) + a$.

(3) ${}^-n \times a = {}^+n \times a$ with its sign reversed.

By these rules the product of any two elements can be determined.

33. From these definitions the following fundamental theorems * can be readily established:

(1902), p. 41, and an extended discussion in Russell, *loc. cit.*, chap. 14. A revised list, in which the number of postulates is reduced to four, is given by A. Padoa, *Rev. de Math.* vol. 8 (1902), p. 48.

* See my two monographs cited in the introduction.

(1) $(a + b) + c = a + (b + c)$. (Associative law for addition.)

(2) $a + b = b + a$.   (Commutative law for addition.)

(3) $(ab)c = a(bc)$.   (Associative law for multiplication.)

(4) $ab = ba$.   (Commutative law for multiplication.)

(5) $a(b + c) = ab + ac$.   (Distributive law for multiplication with respect to addition.)

(6) If x follows 0, then $a + x$ follows a; and if x precedes 0, then $a + x$ precedes a.

(7) If a precedes b, there is an element x which comes after 0 such that $a + x = b$, and an element y which comes before 0 such that $a = b + y$.

(8) If a and b both come after 0, then their product, ab, also comes after 0.

34. As examples of the use of mathematical induction, I give the proofs of the first two theorems in § 33.

Proof of theorem 1. First, *if* the theorem is true for $c = n$, *then* it will be true for $c = n'$, where n' denotes, for the moment, the successor of n.

For, if we denote $^+1$ simply by 1, we have:

$$
\begin{aligned}
(a + b) + n' &= [(a + b) + n] + 1 &&\text{(by definition)}\\
&= [a + (b + n)] + 1 &&\text{(by hypothesis)}\\
&= a + [(b + n) + 1] &&\text{(by definition)}\\
&= a + [b + (n + 1)] &&\text{(by definition)}\\
&= a + (b + n').
\end{aligned}
$$

Secondly, the theorem is clearly true for $c = 1$, by the definition of sum. Therefore, by the first part of the proof, since it is true for $c = 1$, it will be true for $c = 2$; and being true for $c = 2$, it will be true for $c = 3$; and so on. In this way the truth of the theorem for any given value of c can be established, since by the theorem of mathematical induction there is no element c which cannot be reached in this manner.

Proof of theorem 2. We establish first the lemma that $1 + a = a + 1$ by the same method of " proof from n to $n + 1$," using the equations

$$
n' + 1 = (n + 1) + 1 = (1 + n) + 1 = 1 + (n + 1) = 1 + n'.
$$

The proof of the main theorem, that $a + b = b + a$, then follows in a similar way from the equations

$$a + n' = a + (n + 1) = (a + n) + 1 = (n + a) + 1$$
$$= n + (a + 1) = n + (1 + a) = (n + 1) + a = n' + a.$$

The proofs of the remaining theorems involve no new difficulty and can be readily supplied by the reader; when these eight theorems have once been established, the further development of the theory follows lines that are familiar from any text-book of arithmetic and need not be repeated here.* The system (§ 11) thus determined is called, with reference to the arbitrary origin 0, the algebra of *all integers*, with regard to $<$, $+$, and $\times$.

35. Turning now to the progressions,† there are two principal methods of introducing the notions of sum and product, leading to two different systems $(K, <, +, \times)$. In both systems the sums and products are defined *absolutely*, in terms of the relation of order (see § 31).

In the first theory, the progression is denoted by

$$1, 2, 3, \ldots$$

the sums and products being defined as follows:

Sum: $a + 1 =$ the successor of a; $a + 2 =$ the successor of $a + 1$; and so on; in general,

$$a + (\text{the successor of } n) = \text{the successor of } (a + n).$$

Product: $1 \times a = a$; $2 \times a = 1a + a$; and so on; in general,
$$(\text{the successor of } n) \times a = na + a.$$

This system is called the algebra of the *positive integers*, with regard to $<$, $+$, and $\times$.

In the second theory, the progression is denoted by

$$0, 1, 2, 3, \ldots,$$

the sums and products for elements other than 0 being defined as above, and $a + 0 = 0 + a = a$ and $a \times 0 = 0 \times a = 0$.

---

* See O. Stolz and G. A. Gmeiner, *Theoretische Arithmetik* (1901–).

† We pass over the regressions without separate discussion, since whatever is true of a progression is true of a regression if the words " before " and " after," etc., are interchanged.

This system is called the algebra of the *positive integers with zero*, with regard to $<$, $+$, and $\times$.

In both theories, theorems 1–5 of § 33 hold without change, theorems 6–7 have to be slightly modified (in an obvious way), and theorem 8 is superfluous; the further development of the subject need not detain us here.

36. In view of §§ 30–35 it is interesting to note the relation between the system of natural numbers (which has been assumed as familiar, for purposes of illustration, throughout the book), and the ordinal theory of progressions (§ 24). This relation may be stated as follows:

If the class of natural numbers in the usual order — from whatever source it may be derived — is assumed to be a system which satisfies the conditions 1–3, and $N1$–$N3$, and has a first element but no last, then it may be regarded as the *typical example of a progression*, and all the theorems which can be established for any progression will apply to the system of natural numbers. The question whether the system of natural numbers, as commonly conceived, does actually possess the properties demanded in these eight postulates is a question for the psychologist or the epistemologist to decide; as far as the mathematician is concerned, the theory of the natural numbers, in its abstract form, can be derived wholly from the set of postulates just mentioned, the concrete, empirical system of natural numbers being used only as a means of establishing the consistency of these postulates.

Denumerable classes

37. Any infinite class the elements of which can be put into one-to-one correspondence with the elements of a progression (§ 24) is said to be *denumerable* (*abzählbar, dénombrable, enumerable, numerable, countable*).*

In other words, if we assume that the natural numbers in their usual order form a progression (§ 36), a denumerable class is one

* This notion was introduced by Cantor; see *Crelle's Journ. für Math.*, vol. 77 (1873), p. 258, and *Math. Ann.*, vol. 15 (1879), p. 4. For an extension of the notion, see *Math. Ann.*, vol. 23 (1884), p. 456.

which can be put into one-to-one correspondence with the class of all natural numbers.

Every class which appears already ordered in the form of a progression is *ipso facto* a denumerable class; other classes may have to be ingeniously arranged before they can be shown to be denumerable; for example, the class of all proper fractions is shown to be denumerable by the device given in § 19, 6.*

Since any infinite discrete series can be arranged as a progression,† it is obvious that the term progression might be replaced by regression or by unlimited discrete series, in the definition of a denumerable class.

38. The following are the principal theorems concerning denumerable classes:‡

(1) If any finite class is added to a denumerable class, the resulting class will still be denumerable.

For, a progression remains a progression when a finite number of elements are added at the beginning.

(2) A class composed of any finite number of denumerable classes, or even a class composed of a denumerable infinity of denumerable classes, will itself be a denumerable class.

For, if $a_1, a_2, a_3, \ldots$; $b_1, b_2, b_3, \ldots$, etc., are the component classes, we have merely to arrange the elements of the whole class in a two-dimensional array, as in the diagram,

$$a_1, \ a_2, \ a_3, \ \ldots$$
$$b_1, \ b_2, \ b_3, \ \ldots$$
$$c_1, \ c_2, \ c_3, \ \ldots$$
$$\cdot \quad \cdot \quad \cdot$$
$$\cdot \quad \cdot \quad \cdot$$

and then read the table diagonally thus:

1	2	3	4	5	6	$\ldots$
a_1	a_2	b_1	a_3	b_2	c_1	$\ldots$

---

* Cf. G. Faber, *Math. Ann.*, vol. 60 (1905), p. 196.

† To arrange an unlimited discrete series as a progression, take the elements alternately. Of course the correspondence will not be one which preserves the relations of order.

‡ G. Cantor, *Crelle's Journ. für Math.*, vol. 84 (1877), p. 243.

(3) Any collection of non-overlapping three-dimensional regions of space is at most denumerably infinite.*

From this theorem we have the important corollary that *every collection of material objects is at most denumerably infinite;* hence, if we wish to find an example of a non-denumerably infinite class, we must seek it among the classes whose elements are ideal, not material, entities.

The proof of the theorem is as follows:

Case I, when the given collection C lies wholly inside a finite sphere, with center at O and radius r. — Consider the denumerable series of intervals between the numbers

$$V, \quad V/2, \quad V/4, \quad V/8, \quad V/16, \ldots,$$

where V is the volume of the sphere. The number of elements of C which lie between $V/2^{n+1}$ and $V/2^n$ in volume is at most finite (since otherwise the volume of the whole collection C would be greater than V); therefore, by theorem 2, the number of elements in the whole collection C is at most denumerably infinite.

Case II, when the given collection C lies wholly outside the sphere. — This case can be reduced to Case I by an " inversion " of space with respect to the sphere. (An " inversion " transforms every point P outside the sphere into another point P' inside the sphere, such that P' lies on the line OP, and $OP' \times OP = r^2$; this transformation is clearly continuous, so that points which form a connected region outside the sphere will be transformed into points which form a connected region inside the sphere.)

Case III, when the given collection lies partly within and partly without the sphere. — Since each part of the collection is at most denumerably infinite, by Cases I and II, the whole collection will be at most denumerably infinite, by theorem 2.

Analogous theorems hold for areas in a plane, or for segments on a line.

39. A striking example of a denumerable class (though it involves more knowledge of algebra than I wish to assume in this book) is the class of all " algebraic numbers," that is, the class of all complex quantities which can be roots of any algebraic equation with integral coefficients.†

* Cantor, *Math. Ann.*, vol. 20 (1882), p. 117.
† G. Cantor, *Crelle's Journ. für Math.*, vol. 77 (1873), p. 258.

For, the class of values any coefficient can take on is denumerable, hence the class of different equations of the nth degree is denumerable; and since an equation of the nth degree cannot have more than n roots, the class of all the roots of all equations of the nth degree is denumerable; and finally the class of possible degrees is denumerable, so that the whole class of all the roots of all algebraic equations is denumerable.

40. An example of a non-denumerable class is the class of all non-terminating decimal fractions (see § 19, 9). For, if we suppose that this class is denumerable, every non-terminating decimal fraction would have a definite rank in a certain progression; but if we represent this progression as follows:

$$
\begin{array}{ll}
1. & 0.\; a_1\; a_2\; a_3\; \ldots \\
2. & 0.\; b_1\; b_2\; b_3\; \ldots \\
3. & 0.\; c_1\; c_2\; c_3\; \ldots \\
\cdot & \quad \cdot \;\; \cdot \;\; \cdot \;\; \cdot \\
\cdot & \quad \cdot \;\; \cdot \;\; \cdot \;\; \cdot
\end{array}
$$

where each letter (with subscript) denotes one of the digits 0, 1, 2, . . . , 9, we can at once describe non-terminating decimals which do not belong to this list. Thus the decimal

$$
0.\; x_1\; x_2\; x_3\; \ldots ,
$$

where x_1 is different from a_1, x_2 different from b_2, x_3 different from c_3, etc., has no place in the progression, since it differs from the nth decimal in at least the nth digit.[*]

Therefore the class of decimals cannot be denumerable.

[*] G. Cantor, *Jahresbericht der D. Math.-Ver.*, vol. 1 (1892), p. 75.

CHAPTER IV

Dense Series: Especially the Type η of the Rational Numbers

41. In this chapter we consider series $(K, <)$ which satisfy the general postulates 1–3 of § 12, and also the special postulates $H1$ and $H2$, below; the properties here demanded being quite different from the properties of the discrete series considered in the last chapter.

Postulate $H1$.* *If a and b are elements of the class K, and $a < b$, then there is at least one element x in K such that $a < x$ and $x < b$.*

Any series which has this property is said to be *dense*.† Between every two elements of a dense series there will be at least one and therefore an infinity of other elements; so that no element has a successor, and no element a predecessor.

Postulate $H2$. *The class K is denumerable;* that is, the elements of K can be put into one-to-one correspondence with the elements of a progression (§ 37).

Any series which satisfies these two postulates $H1$ and $H2$ is called a *denumerable dense series*, or more briefly, a *rational series*.

A series whose elements form a denumerable class may be called, for brevity, a *denumerable series*.

42. The simplest example of a series which is both denumerable and dense is the class of proper fractions arranged in the usual order (see § 19, 5). For, if $a = m/n$ and $b = p/q$, and $a < b$, then there are elements x which lie between a and b (for example, $x = \dfrac{m + p}{n + q}$,

---

* The letter H is intended to suggest the type η (§ 44).

† Cantor's term is *überall dicht*. Weber uses *dicht*, which Russell replaces by *compact*; *Principles of Mathematics*, vol. 1, p. 271. See however, § 62a.

reduced to its lowest terms); and on the other hand, if we arrange the elements in a two-dimensional array, and then read the table diagonally, as in § 38, we see at once that the class is denumerable.*   (Compare § 19, 6.)

$$\frac{1}{2} \quad \frac{1}{3} \quad \frac{1}{4} \quad \frac{1}{5} \quad \frac{1}{6} \cdots$$

$$\frac{2}{3} \quad \frac{2}{5} \quad \frac{2}{7} \quad \frac{2}{9} \quad \frac{2}{11} \cdots$$

$$\frac{3}{4} \quad \frac{3}{5} \quad \frac{3}{7} \quad \frac{3}{8} \quad \frac{3}{10} \cdots$$

$$\cdot \quad \cdot \quad \cdot \quad \cdot \quad \cdot$$

$$\cdot \quad \cdot \quad \cdot \quad \cdot \quad \cdot$$

43. In every series of this sort we have to do, strictly speaking, with *two* serial relations: with respect to one, the series is dense; with respect to the other, the series is a progression.

44. *The type η.* All denumerable dense series, like all discrete series, can be divided into four groups, distinguished by the presence or absence of first and last elements. All the series of any one of these four groups are ordinally similar, as we shall prove below, and therefore constitute a definite type of order. In particular, the type of denumerable dense series with neither extreme is called by Cantor the *type η.*

The simplest example of a series of the type η is the class of proper fractions in the usual order as already mentioned. By adding an element 0/1 at the beginning, or an element 1/1 at the end, or both, we have an example of a denumerable dense series with a first element, or a last element, or both. Other examples will be given in § 51.

45. We now give the proof † that any two denumerable dense series are ordinally similar, provided they agree in regard to the presence or absence of extreme elements; it will clearly be sufficient to consider two series of the type η, having neither extreme.

* Cantor, *Crelle's Journ. für Math.*, vol. 84 (1877), p. 250.
† Cantor, *Math. Ann.*, vol. 46 (1895), § 9, p. 504.

Let the two given series be A and B; and let the terms of each, when rearranged in the form of a progression, be denoted by

$$a_1, \ a_2, \ a_3, \ \ldots$$

and

$$b_1, \ b_2, \ b_3, \ \ldots .$$

In order to establish a one-to-one correspondence between A and B in a manner preserving order, we proceed step by step, as follows, it being understood that any step is to be omitted if the element considered has already been assigned:

To a_1 assign the element b_1, and to b_1 assign the element a_1.

The elements a_1 and b_1 then divide each of the original series A and B into two sections.

As to a_2, we find in which of the two sections of A it belongs, and assign to it the first of the unused b's which belongs in the corresponding section of B; and as to b_2 (if not already assigned), we find in which section of B it belongs, and assign to it the first of the unused a's which belongs in the corresponding section of A.

The elements a_1 and a_2 then divide the series A into three sections (1st, 2d, and 3d), while the elements b_1 and b_2 divide the series B into three corresponding sections (1st, 2d, and 3d). As to a_3, if not already assigned, we find in which of the three sections of A it belongs, and assign to it the first of the (unused) b's which belongs in the corresponding section of B. Then as to b_3, if not already assigned, we find in which of the three sections of B it belongs, and assign to it the first of the (unused) a's which belongs in the corresponding section of A.

And so on. After $2n$ steps, the first n of the a's will have been assigned and will divide A into $n + 1$ sections, and the first n of the b's will have been assigned and will divide B into $n + 1$ corresponding sections. Then as to a_{n+1}, if not already assigned, we find in which of the $n + 1$ sections of A it belongs, and assign to it the first of the (unused) b's which belongs in the corresponding section of B. And as to b_{n+1}, if not already assigned, we find in which of the $n + 1$ sections of B it belongs, and assign to it the first of the (unused) a's which belongs to the corresponding section of A.

The elements called for at each stage of this process will always exist, since in any series of type η there are elements before and after any given element, and between any two given elements; and by the theorem of mathematical induction as applied to progressions no element of either class is left out in the assignment.

It should be noticed that the correspondence between two series of type η can be set up in an infinite number of ways (compare the case of the unlimited discrete series, § 26).

Segments of series

46. In the following sections we define a few technical terms which will be of great service in the study of dense and continuous series.

In any series (§ 12) a part C (§ 6) which has the following properties we shall call a *fundamental segment* of the series: (1) C is such that if x is any element belonging to C, then every element that precedes x also belongs to C; and (2) C has no last element.

Roughly speaking, a fundamental segment is a part of the series beginning at the beginning, and taking in everything as far as it goes, but having no last element.*

47. A segment in general may be defined as any part C of a series having the following property: if a and b are any two elements belonging to C, then every element that lies between a and b also belongs to C.

A segment C such that if a belongs to C, then every element that $\begin{Bmatrix} \text{precedes} \\ \text{follows} \end{Bmatrix}$ a also belongs to C, is called $\begin{Bmatrix} \text{a lower segment} \\ \text{an upper segment} \end{Bmatrix}$ of the series.†

A fundamental segment, then, is a lower segment which has no last element.

48. It will be noticed at once that in some series no fundamental segments are possible. For example, in a discrete series (§ 21) no fundamental segments are possible, since every subclass which satisfies condition 1 of § 46 either has a last element or includes the whole series. In other cases the number of fundamental segments may be finite. For example, in a series like this:

* Russell's term is *segment* (without distinctive adjective). The notion itself, which is a modification of Dedekind's notion of a cut (1872), was introduced by M. Pasch (*Differential- und Integralrechnung*, 1882), under the name of *Zahlenstrecke*. The term segment was used by Peano in the *Formulaire* for 1899, p. 91, but seems to have been abandoned in later editions.

† Russell, *loc. cit.*, p. 271.

$$1_1, \ 2_1, \ 3_1, \ \ldots; \ 1_2, \ 2_2, \ 3_2, \ \ldots; \ 1_3, \ 2_3, \ 3_3, \ \ldots; \ 1_4, \ 2_4;$$

only three fundamental segments are possible.

In a dense series, however, the class of fundamental segments is always infinite.

49. In connection with fundamental segments the following definition is important: In any series, if there is an element x such that a given fundamental segment coincides with the part of the series which precedes x, then x is called the *limit* of the segment.

If no such element x exists, then the segment has no limit in the given series.

We may then distinguish two kinds of fundamental segments: first, those that have a limit in the given series; and secondly, those that have not.

50. The importance of this distinction between the two kinds of fundamental segments will be clearer after the continuous series have been discussed, in the next chapter. For the present, the most important thing is to see clearly that in some series fundamental segments of the second kind actually exist. To illustrate this point, consider the class of proper fractions arranged in the usual order and take as the subclass C the class of all the fractions m/n for which $2m^2$ is less than n^2; this subclass C will then be a fundamental segment having no limit in the given series.*

To prove this statement,† notice first that C satisfies the definition of a fundamental segment.

For: (1) if m/n belongs to C, and p/q precedes m/n, then p/q also belongs to C, as a brief computation will show; (2) if m/n belongs to C, then there are fractions, — for example,

$$(6m^2 + 1)/6mn, \ddagger$$

---

* In the series of all real numbers, which is not under consideration at this point, the subclass C would be described as the class of all the rational numbers that precede $\sqrt{1/2}$. In verifying the numerical example below, note that since m and n are integers, $2m^2$ must be less than n^2 by at least one; that is, $2m^2 \leqq n^2 - 1$.

† R. Dedekind, *Stetigkeit und irrationale Zahlen*, 1872; H. Weber, *Algebra*, vol. 1, p. 6.

‡ Reduced to its lowest terms.

— which follow m/n and still belong to C, so that C has no last element; and (3) C is neither empty nor contains the whole class, since it contains $1/4$ and does not contain $3/4$.

Furthermore, there is no element x/y which can serve as the limit of the segment. For, first, if $2x^2$ were less than y^2, there would be elements of C, — for example $(6x^2 + 1)/6xy$,* — which came after x/y; secondly, if $2x^2$ were greater than y^2, there would be elements of the series, — for example $(6x^2 - 1)/6xy$,* — which preceded x/y and yet did not belong to C; and thirdly, if $2x^2 = y^2$, we should have an equation containing the factor 2 an odd number of times on the left hand side and an even number of times (if at all) on the right hand side, which is impossible in view of the fact that a natural number can be resolved into prime factors in only one way.

Hence the class C is a fundamental segment which has no limit.†

From this discussion it is clear that Dedekind's postulate (§ 21) is false in every series of type η; for (by § 45) any series of type η may be replaced by the series of proper fractions in the usual order, and if we divide this series into two parts, K_1 and K_2, so that K_1 contains every fraction m/n for which $2m^2 < n^2$, and K_2 all the other fractions, then there will be no element in the series which could serve as the element X required in Dedekind's postulate.

Examples of denumerable dense series

51. In this section we give a number of examples of denumerable dense series; any one of these systems is sufficient to show the consistency of the postulates 1–3, $H1$–$H2$ (compare § 19).

In every denumerable dense series all the postulates $N1$–$N3$ for discrete series (§ 21) are false (compare § 50).

(1) The simplest example of a series of type η is the class of proper fractions in the usual order, as already mentioned in § 44.

Other examples are:

(2) The class of (absolute) rational numbers and

(3) the class of *all* rational numbers (positive, negative or zero), — both being arranged in the usual order.

---

* Reduced to its lowest terms.

† A simpler example of the same sort is provided by the red elements in example 1, § 29.

By an *absolute rational* number we mean an ordered pair of natural numbers, m/n, in which the first number, m, called the numerator, and the second number, n, called the denominator, are relatively prime. By the usual order in this class we mean that m/n is to precede p/q when $m \times q$ is less than $n \times p$.

The class of *all* rationals is then composed of three kinds of elements: (1) the positive rationals, which are absolute rationals affected with the sign $+$; (2) the negative rationals, which are absolute rationals affected with the sign $-$; and (3) an extra element called zero. The "usual order" in this class is precisely defined as follows: of two positive rationals, that one shall precede whose absolute value would precede in the order of absolute rationals; of two negative rationals, that one shall precede whose absolute value would follow in the order of absolute rationals; of two rationals having opposite signs, the negative precedes the positive; and the rational 0 follows every negative rational and precedes every positive rational.

The rationals between 0 and 1/1, or the absolute rationals which precede 1/1, are the proper fractions (§ 19, 5).

If we assign to each absolute rational number p/q the proper fraction $p/(p + q)$, we thereby establish an ordinal correspondence between the series of absolute rationals and the series of proper fractions, in accordance with the theorem of § 45. This done, an ordinal correspondence between the series of absolute rationals and the series of all rationals can be readily established.

(4) As another example of a series of type η, consider the class of points lying within a one-inch square, and such that their distances, x and y, from two sides of the square are proper fractions of an inch; and let the points be arranged in order of magnitude of the x's, or in case of equal x's, in order of magnitude of the y's.

This system clearly satisfies all the postulates for a series of type η; it ought therefore to be possible to exhibit an ordinal correspondence between this system and the series of proper fractions.

This may be done as follows.* Starting with a line AB of fixed length, mark the middle third of it; then mark the middle third of each of the two remaining parts, then the middle third of each of

* Compare § 52, 3, below. The device is due to H. J. S. Smith, *Proc. Lond. Math. Soc.*, vol. 6 (1875), p. 147; cf. G. Cantor, *Math. Ann.*, vol. 21 (1883), p. 590, note 11, and W. H. Young, *Proc. Lond. Math. Soc.*, vol. 34 (1902), p. 286.

the four remaining parts; and so on. The class of marked sections of the line is then a denumerable class, which forms a dense series of type η along the line AB. Now the vertical lines in the given square, corresponding to fractional values of x, also form a denumerable series of type η; hence, by § 45, the class of vertical lines can be brought immediately into ordinal correspondence with the class of marked sections of the line AB. It remains merely to determine on each section the class of what we may call, for the moment, its "fractional" points, that is, the class of points whose

distances from one end of the section are fractional parts of the length of the section; this class of points can then be brought into ordinal correspondence with the "fractional" points of the corresponding vertical line in the square by a suitable magnification.

The given series of points in the square is thus reduced to a dense series of points on the line AB.

—— By a double application of the same method, the "fractional" points within a *cube* can be treated in a similar way.

Examples of series which are not denumerable and dense

52. The following examples of series which fail to satisfy one or both of the postulates $H1$ and $H2$ show that these postulates are independent of each other (compare § 20).

(1) *Denumerable series which are not dense.*

(a) One example of this kind is any unlimited discrete series, such as
$$\ldots, \ -3, \ -2, \ -1, \ \ 0, \ ^{+}1, \ ^{+}2, \ ^{+}3, \ \ldots.$$

By adding an element ^{-}z at the beginning, or an element ^{+}z at the end, or both, we obtain an example with a first or a last element, or both. Progressions and regressions are also examples.

(b) Another example is a class composed of two sets of proper fractions, say red and blue, with the relation of order defined as follows: of two elements which have unequal absolute values that one shall precede which would precede in the usual order of proper fractions, regardless of color; of two elements which have the same absolute value, the red shall precede.

This system is built up by interpolating the elements of one dense series between the elements of another dense series; the resulting series, instead of being "more dense," as one might have been tempted to expect, has lost the property of density altogether, since every red element has an immediate successor.

(2) *Dense series which are not denumerable.*

(a) The class of non-terminating decimal fractions arranged in the usual order (see § 19, 9) is a dense series, which we have already shown to be non-denumerable (§ 40).

(b) Another example is obtained from example (3), below, by omitting the "points of division" that form a part of that class.

(c) For another example, see § 64, 3, (b), footnote.

(3) *A series which is neither denumerable nor dense.*

A striking example of a series which is neither denumerable nor dense may be constructed as follows: * Starting with a line one inch long, mark the middle third of it; then mark the middle third of each of the two remaining parts, then the middle third of each of the four remaining parts, and so on (§ 51, 4); the class considered contains (1) all the points of division, and (2) all the unmarked points of the line; and the order of the points is the natural order along the line.

This series is clearly not dense, since if a and b are the end-points of one of the marked sections, there is no point of the series which lies between them; indeed, no segment of the series will be dense, since every segment (§ 47) will contain a marked section of the line. On the other hand, the class is not denumerable; the proof of this fact (which requires a little more mathematics than is properly assumed in this book) may be outlined as follows:

Let the distance from one end of the line to each point of the line be represented by a ternary fraction (instead of a decimal fraction) of an inch; that is, by a (finite or an infinite) expression of the form

$$0. a_1 a_2 a_3 \ldots ,$$

* Cf. footnote under § 51, 4.

in which a_1 shows the number of thirds, a_2 the number of ninths, a_3 the number of twenty-sevenths, and in general a_n the number of $(1/3^n)$ths; the digits a_1, a_2, a_3, etc., being allowed to take any of the three values 0, 1, and 2. It can then be shown, by a computation involving only an elementary knowledge of the so-called geometric series, that the points of the marked sections of the line (without the points of division) correspond to precisely those ternary fractions in which the digit 1 occurs; the points of our class, therefore, correspond to the ternary fractions in which the digits 0 and 2 only are used; and this class can be shown to be non-denumerable by the method employed in § 40 for the decimal fractions.

Arithmetical operations among the elements of a dense series

53. In conclusion, we notice that since the theorem of mathematical induction does not apply to dense series, it is not possible to give purely ordinal definitions for the sums and products of the elements of such a series. All that we could do in this direction would be to define the sums and products of the elements of some particular dense series, say the series of the rational numbers in the usual order, by the use of some extra-ordinal properties peculiar to that series; then since all series of type η are ordinally similar, the definitions set up in the standard series could be transferred to any other series of the same type by a one-to-one correspondence. This method would be wholly inadequate, however, since the ordinal correspondence could be set up in an infinite number of ways. Indeed, in the case of a series of type η (without extreme elements), unless we introduce some other fundamental notion beside the notion of order, the elements have *no ordinal properties by which we can tell them apart*. It is better, therefore, to introduce addition and multiplication as fundamental notions of the system (compare § 11), and define their properties by postulates; this problem is, however, beyond the scope of the present work.*

* See, for example, my two monographs cited in the introduction.

CHAPTER V

Continuous Series: Especially the Type θ of the Real Numbers

54. In the preceding chapters we have considered the discrete series (§ 21) and the dense series (§ 41); we turn now to the study of the linear continuous series, which are the most important for algebra.

A *continuous series* in general is defined as any series which satisfies postulates 1–3 of § 12, and also Dedekind's postulate ($C1$, below) and the postulate of density ($C2$); a *linear* continuous series is then any continuous series which satisfies also a further condition, which I shall call the postulate of linearity ($C3$).

POSTULATE $C1$.* (*Dedekind's postulate.*) *If K_1 and K_2 are any two non-empty parts of K, such that every element of K belongs either to K_1 or to K_2 and every element of K_1 precedes every element of K_2, then there is at least one element X in K such that:*

(1) *any element that precedes X belongs to K_1, and*

(2) *any element that follows X belongs to K_2.*

This is the same as postulate $N1$ in § 21.

POSTULATE $C2$. (*Postulate of density.*) *If a and b are elements of the class K, and $a \prec b$, then there is at least one element x in K such that $a \prec x$ and $x \prec b$.*

This is the same as postulate $H1$ in § 41.

POSTULATE $C3$.† (*Postulate of linearity.*) *The class K contains a denumerable subclass R (§ 37) in such a way that between any two elements of the given class K there is an element of R.*

---

* R. Dedekind, *loc. cit.* (1872).

† G. Cantor, *loc. cit.* (1895), § 11, p. 511. O. Veblen replaces this postulate of linearity by two other postulates which he calls the pseudo-Archimedean postulate and the postulate of uniformity [*Trans. Amer. Math. Soc.*, vol. 6 (1905), pp. 165–171]. See also R. E. Root, *Limits in terms of order*, *Trans. Amer. Math. Soc.*, vol. 15 (1914), pp. 51–71.

The consistency and independence of these postulates will be discussed in § 63 and § 64; postulate $C2$ is clearly redundant whenever postulate $C3$ is assumed.

55. The most familiar example of a linear continuous series is the class of points on a line, say one inch long, the relation $a < b$ signifying that a lies on the left of b. Dedekind's postulate is satisfied in this system, since if K_1 and K_2 are two parts of the kind described in the postulate, there will be a point of division on the line (either the last point of K_1 or the first point of K_2), which will serve as the point X demanded in the postulate. The postulate of density is also clearly satisfied, since between any two points of the line other points can be found. Finally, to see that the postulate of linearity holds, take as the subclass R the class of all points of the line whose distances from one end are rational fractions of an inch.

An example of a continuous series which is not linear is the class of all points (x, y) of a square (including the boundaries), arranged

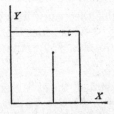

in order of magnitude of the x's, or, in case of equal x's, in order of magnitude of the y's. This series is continuous (satisfying postulates $C1$ and $C2$), but no subclass R of the kind demanded in postulate $C3$ is possible within it; for, if there were such a subclass it would have to contain elements corresponding to every point of the base of the square and therefore could not be denumerable (see § 58 below).

Other examples, not depending on geometric intuition, will be given in § 63 and § 64, 3.

56. With the aid of the following definition, we may state two theorems that hold for all continuous series.

Definition. Let C be any non-empty subclass in any series $(K, \prec)$; if there is an element X in the series such that:

(1) there is no element of C which follows X, while

(2) if Y is any element preceding X there is at least one element of C which follows Y: — then this element X is called the *upper limit* of the subclass C.

If the subclass C happens to have a last element, this element itself will be the upper limit of the subclass. If C has no last element, it may or may not have an upper limit; if it has an upper limit, then this upper limit is the element which comes *next after* the subclass C in the given series.*

Theorem 1. *In any continuous series, if C is any subclass all of whose elements precede a given element, then C will have an upper limit in the series.*

Briefly, this theorem tells us that in any continuous series, every subclass which has *any* upper bound will have a *lowest* upper bound, — the terms "upper limit" and "lowest upper bound" being synonymous.

The full meaning of this theorem will be clearer after a study of the examples given in §§ 63–64 of series that are and those that are not continuous (compare also § 50); the formal proof is easily given, as follows:

Under the conditions stated, the given series can be divided into two non-empty subclasses, K_1 and K_2, the first containing every element that is equaled or surpassed by any element of C, and the second containing all the other elements; † then by Dedekind's postulate there must be at least one element X "dividing" K_1 from K_2; moreover, there cannot be two such elements, for if there were, one would be the last element of K_1 and the other the first element of K_2, so that no element would lie between them (contrary to the postulate of density). This dividing element X is then the element required in the theorem.

* It should be noticed that this definition of a limit of a subclass in general is consistent with the definition already given for the limit of a fundamental segment (§ 49).

† The subclass K_2 will not be an empty class, since by hypothesis there is at least one element in K which follows all the elements of C.

Similarly, we may define the *lower limit* of a subclass, and prove the analogous theorem:

THEOREM 2. *In any continuous series, if C is any subclass all of whose elements follow a given element, then C will have a lower limit in the series.*

That is, in any continuous series, every subclass which has *any* lower bound will have a *highest* lower bound, or lower limit.

COROLLARY. *In any continuous series which has a first and a last element, every subclass will have both an upper limit and a lower limit in the series.*

57. The following theorem gives us another form of the definition of continuous series.

THEOREM.* *In the definition of a continuous series (§ 54), Dedekind's postulate may be replaced by the demand that every fundamental segment shall have a limit (§ 49).*

For, if the elements of the whole series are divided into two subclasses K_1 and K_2 as in the hypothesis of Dedekind's postulate, then K_1 (or K_1 without its last element, if it happens to have one) will be a fundamental segment, and the limit of this segment will correspond to the element X in Dedekind's postulate.

58. The next theorem concerns the infinitude of the elements of a continuous series.

THEOREM. *The elements of any continuous series (§ 54) form an infinite class which is not denumerable (§ 37).*

The proof, which is due to Cantor,† is as follows:

Suppose a given continuous series to be denumerable; then without disturbing the order of the elements we may attach to each one a definite natural number, using the notation $a(n)$ to represent the element corresponding to the number n.

We may assume without loss of generality that the elements have been so numbered that the element $a(1)$ precedes the element $a(2)$.

Then let p_1 and q_1 be the smallest numbers for which $a(p_1)$ and $a(q_1)$ lie between $a(1)$ and $a(2)$, and assume that the elements have been so numbered that $a(p_1) \prec a(q_1)$; then

$$a(1) \prec a(p_1) \quad \prec \quad a(q_1) \prec a(2).$$

* Cf. a remark due to Whitehead in Russell's *Principles of Mathematics*, vol. 1 (1903), p. 299, footnote.

† G. Cantor, *Crelle's Journ. für Math.*, vol. 77 (1874), p. 260.

Next, let p_2 and q_2 be the smallest numbers for which $a(p_2)$ and $a(q_2)$ lie between $a(p_1)$ and $a(q_1)$ and assume $a(p_2) \prec a(q_2)$, so that

$$a(1) \prec a(p_1) \prec a(p_2) \quad \prec \quad a(q_2) \prec a(q_1) \prec a(2).$$

And so on. In general, let p_{k+1} and q_{k+1} be the smallest numbers for which $a(p_{k+1})$ and $a(q_{k+1})$ lie between $a(p_k)$ and $a(q_k)$, and assume $a(p_{k+1}) \prec a(q_{k+1})$. In this way we determine a progression of elements $a(p_k)$ and a regression of elements $a(q_k)$, such that

$$a(1) \prec a(p_1) \prec a(p_2) \prec \ldots \prec \ldots \prec a(q_2) \prec a(q_1) \prec a(2).$$

Now since the series is continuous, the progression in question ought to have an upper limit (§ 56); but there is no element $a(n)$ which can serve as this upper limit, for if any element $a(n)$ is proposed, we can clearly carry the process just indicated so far that $a(n)$ will lie outside the interval $a(p_k) \ldots \ldots \ldots a(q_k)$.

Therefore if the series is denumerable it cannot be continuous, and the theorem is proved.

59. The theorems of §§ 56–58 hold for all continuous series; the following theorems apply only to the linear continuous series.

THEOREM. *Every linear continuous series* (§ 54) *contains a subclass R of type* η (§ 44), *such that between any two elements of the given series there is an element of R.*

For, the denumerable subclass R whose existence is demanded in postulate $C3$, or the same subclass without its extreme elements if it has them, is clearly of type η (the type of the rational numbers).

This subclass R of type η may be called the *skeleton*, or *framework*, of the given series; the elements which belong to R may be called, for the moment, the *rational* elements, and those that do not belong to R the *irrational* elements of the series.

Since the class of all the elements of any continuous series is non-denumerably infinite (§ 58), it is clear that the rational elements of a linear continuous series cannot exhaust the series; in fact the class of irrational elements in any such series will itself be non-denumerably infinite (compare § 38).

60. The most important property of the rational elements is given in the following theorem, which follows immediately from § 56:

THEOREM. *In any linear continuous series, every element a (unless it be the first) determines a fundamental segment (§ 46) of the so-called rational elements, namely, the series of all the rationals preceding a; and conversely, every fundamental segment of rationals determines an element of the given series, namely, the upper limit of the segment (§ 56).*

The rational elements of the given series correspond to the fundamental segments which have limits in the series of rationals; the irrational elements correspond to the segments which have no limits in the series of rationals (§§ 49, 50). The denumerable dense series considered in the preceding chapter are not continuous, since, as we have seen in § 50, they contain fundamental segments which have no limits; the theorem thus brings out clearly the sense in which the linear continuous series are " richer " in elements than the denumerable dense series.

61. *The type θ.* The linear continuous series, like the discrete series or the denumerable dense series, can be divided into four groups, distinguished by the presence or absence of extreme elements; all the series of any one group are ordinally similar (see below), and therefore constitute a definite type of order. In particular, a *linear continuous series* (§ 54) *which has both a first and a last element* is called by Cantor a series of the *type θ,* or the type of the *linear continuum.**

The proof that any two series of type θ are ordinally similar follows readily from the analogous theorem in regard to series of type η (§ 45).* For, by § 59 each of the given series of type θ will contain a subclass of " rational " elements of type η; by § 45 these subclasses of rationals can be brought into ordinal correspondence with each other; and by § 60 every element (except the first) of each of the given series is uniquely determined as the limit of a fundamental segment of rationals.

It should be noticed, however, that this correspondence can be set up in an infinite number of ways, since not only the selection of rational elements from the given series, but also the correspondence between the two sets of rational elements, can be determined in an infinite number of ways.

---

* G. Cantor, *loc. cit.* (1895), § 11, p. 511. Russell, *loc. cit.*, chap. 36.

62. Since the definition of the type θ here adopted differs in manner of approach, though not in substance, from the definition given by Cantor, I add, in this section, a statement of Cantor's definition in its original form.*

Every progression or regression which belongs to a given series is called by Cantor a *fundamental sequence* (*Fundamentalreihe*); any element which is the limit of any fundamental sequence (upper limit in the case of a progression, lower limit in the case of a regression), is called a *principal element* (*Hauptelement*) of the series.† If every fundamental sequence which exists in a given series has a limit in the series, the series is said to be *closed* (*abgeschlossen*); if every element of the series is the limit of some fundamental sequence, the series is said to be *dense-in-itself* (*insichdicht*); and any series which is both dense-in-itself and closed is said to be *perfect* (*perfekt*). Finally, if a series is such that between any two elements there are other elements, the series is said to be *dense* (*überalldicht*).

The following theorems follow at once from these definitions:

(1) If a series is closed, it will satisfy Dedekind's postulate (§ 54).

(2) If a series satisfies Dedekind's postulate, and has both extreme elements, it will be closed.

On the other hand, the following facts should be noticed:

(3) A series may satisfy Dedekind's postulate, and still not be closed, as witness the series of all integers, or the series of all real numbers.‡

(4) A series may be perfect (that is, dense-in-itself and closed), and not be dense; as witness the series discussed in § 52, 3 (with end-points), or the series of all real numbers from 0 to 3 inclusive with the omission of those between 1 and 2.

* G. Cantor, *loc. cit.* (1895), §§ 10–11, p. 508. An earlier definition of the arithmetical continuum given by Cantor in *Math. Ann.*, vol. 5 (1872), p. 123 [cf. *ibid.*, vol. 21 (1883), pp. 572–576], involved extra-ordinal considerations, and need not concern us here.

† This definition of a fundamental sequence is inaccurately quoted by Veblen (*loc. cit.*, p. 171), who leaves out the regressions. Thus, in the series

$$2', \ 1'; \ \ldots, \ ^-3, \ ^-2, \ ^-1, \ 0, \ ^+1, \ ^+2, \ ^+3, \ \ldots; \ 1'', \ 2''$$

the element 1′ would be a principal element according to Cantor's definition, but not according to Veblen's. [The same word, *Fundamentalreihe*, has been used by Cantor in another connection, in discussing irrational numbers; *Math. Ann.*, vol. 21 (1883), p. 567].

‡ It is therefore perhaps unfortunate to speak of Dedekind's postulate as the postulate of closure.

(5) A series may be dense-in-itself and dense, and not be closed, as for example the series of rational numbers (with or without extreme elements).

(6) A series may be dense and closed and not be dense-in-itself,* as for example the series $V + 0 + {}^*V$, where V denotes, for the moment, Veblen's series described in § 64, 3, b, and ${}^*V$ the same series in reverse order. Here the element 0 is not the limit of any fundamental sequence, since every progression in V has a limit in V, and every regression in ${}^*V$ has a limit in ${}^*V$, if we admit the validity of Cantor's reasoning in regard to the transfinite well-ordered series (§ 83).

(7) A series may be perfect (that is, dense-in-itself and closed), and yet have no last element and no first element, as for example the series ${}^*V + V$. Here V and ${}^*V$ have the meanings just explained.†

By the aid of these definitions, Cantor defines a *series of type θ* by the following two conditions:

(A) *the series must be perfect* (that is, dense-in-itself and closed); and

(B) *the series must contain a denumerable subclass R in such a way that between any two elements of the given series there is an element of R.*

Every series which satisfies condition B will clearly be dense. The agreement between this definition and that given in § 61 may be readily established by the reader. The use of Dedekind's postulate instead of the postulate of closure implies the use of fundamental segments instead of the fundamental sequences; this modification of Cantor's method seems to me desirable, since every segment determines a unique element, and every element determines a unique segment, while in the case of the sequences, although every sequence determines a unique element, it is not true that every element determines a unique sequence.‡ I have preferred Dedekind's postulate to the postulate of § 57 merely because of its greater symmetry.

* Compare a question raised by Russell, *loc. cit.*, p. 300. The series given in the footnote on the preceding page is a closed series which is neither dense nor dense-in-itself.

† Cf. Hans Hahn, *Monatshefte für Math. und Phys.*, vol. 21 (1910), *Literaturberichte*, p. 26.

‡ It can be shown, however, that the class of fundamental sequences in any continuous series has the same " cardinal number " (§ 88) as the class of elements in the series itself (compare § 71).

62a. To avoid possible confusion with § 62, it may be well to mention here the definitions of some of the terms used in the theory of sets of points,* which is closely related to the theory of series.

A (linear) *set of points* is a collection of points selected in any manner from the points of a straight line. Any point P of the line is called a *cluster-point (limit-point, point of condensation)* of the set, if in every interval which contains P as an interior point there are points of the set. A cluster point may or may not belong to the set. A set is called *closed (abgeschlossen)* if every cluster point of the set belongs to the set. A set is called *dense-in-itself* if every point of the set is a cluster point of the set. A *perfect* set is one which is both closed and dense-in-itself. A set is called *everywhere-dense* if between every two distinct points of the line there are points of the set.

A set can be perfect and nowhere dense, as, for example, the set described in § 52, 3. Every perfect set can be put into one-to-one correspondence (sacrificing order) with the set of elements in a linear continuum.

The *derived set (Ableitung)* of a given set is the set composed of all the cluster points of the given set. In the case of a perfect set, the derived set is the same as the given set.

A set is called *compact* if every subclass in the set has a cluster point in the set. (Contrast Russell's use of " compact "; § 41, footnote.)

Examples of linear continuous series

63. The following examples serve to establish the consistency of the postulates of the present chapter (§ 54; compare § 19); in all but the first of them we avoid making any appeal to geometric intuition.

(1) The simplest geometric example of a linear continuous series is the series of all points on a line, already considered in § 55.

The most important non-geometrical examples are:

(2) The class of (absolute) real numbers, arranged in the usual order; and

(3) The class of *all* real numbers (positive, negative, and zero), arranged in the usual order.

---

* For references to recent work in this field see R. E. Root, *Trans. Amer. Math. Soc.*, vol. 15 (1914), pp. 51–71; some of the standard treatises are mentioned in a footnote under § 73.

By the *absolute real numbers* we mean the class of all fundamental segments (§ 46) in the series of absolute rational numbers (§ 51, 2); and by the usual order within this class we mean that a segment a shall precede a segment b when a is a part of b.*

This system clearly satisfies the general conditions for a series (§ 12), since if a and b are any two distinct fundamental segments of any dense series, one of them must be a part of the other, and the relation of inclusion is transitive. Further, the series is dense; for, if a segment a is part of a segment b, there will always be rationals belonging to b and not to a; a segment x containing the segment a and some of these rationals will then lie " between " the segments a and b. To show that Dedekind's postulate is also satisfied, suppose that the whole series K is divided in any way into

* This is the definition adopted by Russell (*loc. cit.*, chap. 33); it was first given in this form by M. Pasch (*Differential- und Integralrechnung*, 1882), his *Zahlenstrecke* (fundamental segment of rationals) being a modification of Dedekind's *Schnitt* or *cut* (1872). Similar definitions have been given by Dedekind (1872), Cantor (1872), Peano (1899), and others; a historical account is given by Peano in *Rev. de Math.*, vol. 6 (1899), pp. 126–140. The construction of the system of (absolute) real numbers may be briefly described as follows (confining ourselves to the positive numbers): (1) the *integers* are the natural numbers, assumed as known; (2) the *rationals* are pairs of integers; and (3) the *reals* are classes (fundamental segments) of rationals. As a matter of convenience in notation, a pair of integers in which the denominator is 1 is represented by the numerator alone; rational numbers of this form are said to be *integral*, while all other rational numbers are called *fractional*. Again, a fundamental segment which has a limit in the series of rationals is represented by the same symbol as its limit; real numbers of this form are said to be *rational*, while all other real numbers are called *irrational* (compare § 50). This notation, however, should not be interpreted as meaning that the class of real numbers *includes* the class of rationals, or that the class of rational numbers *includes* the class of integers. On the contrary, while the " integral number 2 " means simply the second number in the natural series, the " rational number 2 " means the pair of natural numbers 2 and 1, and " the real number 2 " means the class of all rational numbers which precede the rational number 2/1. The rules by which the sum and product of two real numbers are defined do not concern us, in this discussion of the purely ordinal theory; see O. Stolz and J. A. Gmeiner, *Theoretische Arithmetik* (1901–); J. Tannery, *Introduction à la théorie des fonctions* (2nd edit., 1904); H. Weber and J. Wellstein, *Encyclopädie der Elementar-Mathematik* (vol. 1, 1903); E. V. Huntington, *Trans. Amer. Math. Soc.*, vol. 6 (1905), pp. 209–229, or the two monographs cited in the introduction; A. Loewy, *Lehrbuch der Algebra* (1915).

two parts K_1 and K_2 such that every element of K_1 precedes every element of K_2; then the class of all rationals which belong to any element of K_1 will be a fundamental segment in the series of rationals, and will be the element X demanded in the postulate. Finally, the series is a *linear* continuous series, since we may take as the required subclass R all the elements of K which have limits in the series of rationals (§ 49).

By the series of *all* real numbers (positive, negative, or zero) we then mean a series built up from the series of absolute real numbers in the same way as the series of all rationals was built up from the series of absolute rationals in § 51, 3. Or again, all real numbers may be defined as fundamental segments of the series of all rationals, just as the absolute real numbers are defined as fundamental segments of the series of absolute rationals.

In the series of real numbers we have thus constructed an artificial system which certainly satisfies all the conditions for a linear continuous series (§ 54); there can therefore be no doubt that those conditions are free from inconsistency.* If we assume as geometrically evident that the series of all points on a line an inch long also satisfies these conditions, then an ordinal correspondence can be established between the real numbers and the points of the line, in accordance with § 61 (taking as the " rational " points of the line those points whose distances from one end of the line are proper fractions of an inch); but in setting up this correspondence we must recognize that the continuity of the series of points on the line is an assumption which is not capable of direct experimental verification.

(4) Another example of a linear continuous series is the class of all non-terminating decimal fractions, arranged in the usual order (§ 19, 9; § 40).

This series is dense; for, suppose a and b are any two of the decimals such that $a \prec b$; let β_k be the first digit of b which is greater than the corresponding digit of a, and let β_n be the first

* Cf. H. Weber, *Algebra*, vol. 1, p. 7, where the real numbers are defined (after Dedekind) as " cuts " in the series of rationals, instead of as fundamental segments of rationals. (A *cut* is simply a rule for dividing a series K into two non-empty parts K_1 and K_2, such that every element of K_1 precedes every element of K_2, while K_1 and K_2 together exhaust the series K.)

digit beyond β_k which is different from 0; then any decimal x in which the first $n-1$ digits are the same as in b, while the nth digit is less by one than β_n, will lie between a and b. Further, the series satisfies Dedekind's postulate; for, if K_1 and K_2 are the given sub-classes, we may determine the decimal $X = .\xi_1\xi_2\xi_3 \ldots$ as follows: ξ_1 is the largest digit which occurs in the first place of any decimal belonging to K_1; ξ_2 is the largest digit which occurs in the second place of any decimal beginning with ξ_1 and belonging to K_1; ξ_3 is the largest digit which occurs in the third place of any decimal beginning with $\xi_1\xi_2$ and belonging to K_1; and so on. Finally, the series is linear, since we may take as the subclass R the class of those decimals in which all the places after any given place are filled with 9's. — The series, as we notice, contains a last element (.999 . . .), but no first.

(5) As a final example we mention the series described in § 19, 8, namely: K = the class of all possible infinite classes of the natural numbers, no number being repeated in any one class; with the relation $<$ so defined that $a < b$ when the smallest number in a is less than the smallest number in b, or, if the smallest n numbers of a and b are the same, when the $(n+1)$st number of a is less than the $(n+1)$st number of b.

This series is continuous, as the reader may readily verify; and it may be shown that it satisfies the postulate of linearity, since we may take as the subclass R the class of all the elements in which only a finite number of the natural numbers are absent. We notice also that the series contains a first element (namely the class of *all* the natural numbers), but no last element.

This example is particularly interesting as showing how a linear continuous series can be built up directly from the natural numbers, without making use of the rationals.*

Examples of series which are not linear continuous series

64. The examples given in this section serve to show (compare § 20) that postulates $C1$ and $C2$ (§ 54) are independent of each other, and that postulate $C3$ is independent of both of them. Postulate $C2$, on the other hand, is clearly a consequence of postulate $C3$.

* B. Russell, *Principles of Mathematics*, vol. 1, p. 299.

(1) *Dense series which do not satisfy Dedekind's postulate.*

(*a*) Denumerable series which are dense but do not satisfy Dedekind's postulate are given in § 51.

(*b*) A non-denumerable example of the same sort is the series of all the points on a line with the exception of some single point; or better, the series described in § 52, 2, *b*.

(2) *Series which satisfy Dedekind's postulate, but are not dense.*

(*a*) The series described in § 52, 3 (consisting of the ternary fractions in which the digits 0 and 2 only are used) is not dense, but can readily be shown to satisfy the postulate of Dedekind.

(*b*) Any discrete series is also an example of this kind.

(3) *Continuous series which are not linear.*

(*a*) Let K be the class of all couples (x, y), where x and y are real numbers from 0 to 1 inclusive; and let $(x_1, y_1) < (x_2, y_2)$ when $x_1 < x_2$, or when $x_1 = x_2$ and $y_1 < y_2$. This series is a continuous series (satisfying $C1$ and $C2$); but it is not a linear continuous series, since no denumerable subclass R of the kind demanded in postulate $C3$ is possible within it. (The same example, in geometric form, has been mentioned already in § 55; other examples of a similar kind will occur in § 70.)

(*b*) Let ω_1 (or Ω) be the smallest of the well-ordered series of Cantor's third class (see § 83, below), and connect each element with the next following element by a linear continuous series; the resulting series, which has been proposed by Veblen,* is continuous but contains no denumerable subclass R of the kind demanded in postulate $C3$, since every denumerable subclass in the series has an upper limit in the series (cf. § 85).

(4) *A series which is not continuous and not dense.*

As a final example of a series which is not continuous, we mention a class K composed of two sets of real numbers, say red and blue, with a relation of order defined as follows: of two elements

---

* O. Veblen, *Trans. Amer. Math. Soc.*, vol. 6 (1905), p. 169. Another interesting series may be made from the series Ω by connecting each element with the next following element by a series of type η; this series is dense and dense-in-itself but not denumerable and not closed (cf. § 62, 5).

which have unequal numerical values, that one shall precede which would precede in the usual order of real numbers, regardless of color; of two elements which have the same numerical value, the red shall precede.

This system is built up by interpolating the elements of one continuous series between the elements of another continuous series; the resulting series, instead of being "more continuous" as one might have been tempted to expect, is no longer even dense, since every red element has an immediate successor (compare § 52, 1, *b*).

Arithmetical operations among the elements of a continuous series

65. In the case of continuous series as in the case of dense series it is not possible to give purely ordinal definitions of the sums and products of the elements; for, unless some other fundamental notion besides the notion of order is introduced, the elements of these series (except extreme elements) have *no ordinal properties by which we can tell them apart* (compare § 53). We might, to be sure, define sums and products of the elements of some particular series (like the series of real numbers, in the usual order) by the use of extra-ordinal properties peculiar to that series, and then transfer these definitions to other series of the same type by a one-to-one ordinal correspondence; but this method would be wholly inadequate, since the ordinal correspondence could be set up in an infinite number of ways. To construct a *completely determinate* continuous system it is therefore necessary to introduce some further notions, like addition and multiplication, besides the notion of order, as fundamental notions of the system.*

* See for example my set of postulates for ordinary complex algebra, *Trans. Amer. Math. Soc.*, vol. 6 (1905), pp. 209–229, especially § 8, or my monograph on *The Fundamental Propositions of Algebra*, cited in the introduction; or my postulates for absolute continuous magnitude, *Trans. Amer. Math. Soc.*, vol. 3 (1902), pp. 264–279.

CHAPTER VI

CONTINUOUS SERIES OF MORE THAN ONE DIMENSION, WITH A NOTE ON MULTIPLY ORDERED CLASSES

66. In the preceding chapters we have studied various kinds of series, or simply ordered classes (§ 12), — especially the linear continuous series (§ 54). In the following chapter we consider briefly some kinds of continuous series which are not linear, and add a short note on multiply ordered classes.

Continuous series of more than one dimension.*

67. We shall use the term *one-dimensional framework* or *skeleton* (R_1) to denote a *series of type η*, that is, a denumerable dense series without extreme elements (§ 44). A *one-dimensional, or linear, continuous series* is then any continuous series which contains a framework R_1 in such a way that between any two elements of the given series there are elements of R_1 (§ 59).

Again, a *two-dimensional framework*, R_2, is any series formed from a one-dimensional continuous series by replacing each element of that series by a series of type η; and a *two-dimensional continuous series* is any continuous series which contains a framework R_2 in the same way.

And so on. In general, an *n-dimensional framework*, R_n, is any series formed from an $(n - 1)$-dimensional continuous series by replacing each element of that series by a series of type η; and an *n-dimensional continuous series* is any continuous series which contains a framework R_n in such a way that between any two elements of the given series there are elements of R_n.

* The study of the multi-dimensional continuous series was proposed by Cantor in *Math. Ann.*, vol. 21, p. 590, note 12 (1883), but seems never to have been carried out in detail. It would be interesting to extend the discussion to continuous series of a transfinite number of dimensions (cf. § 88).

68. By a *k-dimensional section* of any continuous series we shall mean any segment (§ 47) which forms by itself a *k*-dimensional continuous series, but is not a part of any other such segment.*

In an *n*-dimensional continuous series each one-dimensional section, unless it be the $\frac{\text{first}}{\text{last}}$, will have a $\frac{\text{first}}{\text{last}}$ element, and these elements taken in order will form an $(n-1)$-dimensional continuous series. And so in general: each *k*-dimensional section, unless it be the $\frac{\text{first}}{\text{last}}$, will have a $\frac{\text{first}}{\text{last}}$ $(k-1)$-dimensional section, and these $(k-1)$-dimensional sections taken in order will be the elements of an $(n-k)$-dimensional continuous series.

69. As already noted, there are four different types of one-dimensional continuous series, distinguished by the presence or absence of extreme elements; in particular, a one-dimensional continuous series with both a first and a last element is called a series of *type θ* (§ 61).

A two-dimensional continuous series may or may not have a first one-dimensional section, and that section in turn may or may not have a first element. Similarly, there may or may not be a last one-dimensional section, which in turn may or may not have a last element. There are therefore nine different types of such series, distinguished by their initial and terminal properties. In particular, a two-dimensional continuous series with both a first and a last element we may call a series of *type θ²* (since it may be formed from a series of type *θ* by replacing each element by another series of type *θ*).†

And so on. In general, there will be $(n+1)^2$ different types of *n*-dimensional continuous series, distinguished by their initial and terminal properties. In particular, an *n*-dimensional continuous series which has both a first and a last element may be called a series of *type θⁿ*.

* We may speak of a section of a framework R_n, as well as of a section of a continuous series. A "zero-dimensional" section would be, of course, a single element. — If preferred, the word *constituent* may be used instead of *section*.

† Cf. Cantor's notation for the "product" of two well-ordered series (§ 86).

The proof that any two series of the same type are ordinally similar, and that all the types are distinct, is readily obtained by an extension of the methods used in §§ 45 and 61.

70. An example of an n-dimensional continuous series is a class whose elements are sets of real numbers $(x_1, x_2, x_3, \ldots, x_n)$, where x_1 is any real number, and $x_2, x_3, \ldots, x_n$ are restricted to the interval from 0 to 1 inclusive; the elements of the class being arranged primarily in order of the x_1's; or in case of equal x_1's, in order of the x_2's; or in case of equal x_1's and equal x_2's, in order of the x_3's; etc.

If $n = 1$, 2, or 3, the elements of this class can be represented geometrically: (1) by the points on a line; (2) by the points of a plane region bounded by two parallel lines; and (3) by the points of a space region bounded by a square prismatic surface. If n is greater than 3, no simple geometrical interpretation is possible.

71. Although the various types of series just considered are all distinct as types of order, yet it is important to notice that *the class of elements* of an n-dimensional continuous series can be put into one-to-one correspondence with *the class of elements* of a one-dimensional continuous series, if the relation of order is sacrificed; or, in the terminology of modern geometry, *the points of all space (of any number of dimensions) can be put into one-to-one correspondence with the points of a line.* One of Cantor's most interesting early discoveries was a device for actually setting up this correspondence; we give a sketch of the method for the case of two dimensions.*

As a preliminary step, we notice that a one-to-one correspondence can be set up between the points of any two lines, of length a and b, with or without end-points. For, each line can be divided into a denumerable set of segments of lengths equal, say, to $\frac{1}{2}$, $\frac{1}{4}$, $\frac{1}{8}$, $\ldots$ of the length of the line; a one-to-one correspondence can be established between the two sets of segments, and then (as in § 3) between the interior points of each segment of one set and the interior points of the corresponding segment of the other set; and a one-to-one correspondence can also be established between the two sets of points of division.

* Cantor, *Crelle's Journ. für Math.*, vol. 84, pp. 242–258 (1877); cf. *Math. Ann.*, vol. 46, p. 488 (1895).

Consider now the points (x, y) within a square one inch on a side $(0 < x < 1, 0 < y < 1)$, and the points t on a line say three inches long $(0 < t < 3)$; and divide each third of the line t into a denumerable set of segments of lengths $\frac{1}{2}, \frac{1}{4}, \frac{1}{8}, \ldots$ of an inch. A one-to-one correspondence between the points of the square and the points of the line can then be established as follows:

(1) The points (x, y) for which x and y are both rational form a denumerable set, and can therefore be put into one-to-one correspondence with the " rational " points of the line — that is, the points for which t is rational.

(2) The points (x, y) for which x is rational and y irrational are the " irrational " points of a denumerable set of vertical lines, and can therefore be put into one-to-one correspondence with the " irrational " points of the denumerable set of segments which occupies, say, the last third of the line.

(3) Similarly the points (x, y) for which y is rational and x irrational can be put into one-to-one correspondence with the " irrational " points of the middle third of the line.

(4) Finally, the points for which x and y are both irrational can be put into one-to-one correspondence with the " irrational " points of the first third of the line. For, every *irrational* number a between 0 and 1 can be expressed as a *non-terminating* simple continued fraction, $a = [a_1, a_2, a_3, \ldots]$, that is:

$$a = \cfrac{1}{a_1 + \cfrac{1}{a_2 + \cfrac{1}{a_3 + \ldots,}}}$$

where $a_1, a_2, a_3, \ldots$ are positive integers; so that to the point

$$x = [x_1, x_2, x_3, \ldots],$$
$$y = [y_1, y_2, y_3, \ldots]$$

in the square we can assign the point

$$t = [x_1, y_1, x_2, y_2, x_3, y_3, \ldots]$$

on the line; while inversely, to the point

$$t = [t_1, t_2, t_3, \ldots]$$

on the line we can assign the point

$$x = [t_1, t_3, t_5, \ldots],$$
$$y = [t_2, t_4, t_6, \ldots]$$

in the square.

Thus the correspondence between the points of the square and the points of the line is complete; and the method is easily extended to any number of dimensions, finite or denumerably infinite.

Note on multiply ordered classes

72. A *multiply ordered class* is a system (§ 11) consisting of a class K the elements of which may be ordered according to several different serial relations.

For example, a class of musical tones may be arranged in order according to pitch, or according to intensity, or according to duration. Again, the class of points in space may be ordered in various ways according to their distances from three fixed planes.

A multiply ordered class may also be called a *multiple series;* but a system of this kind is not strictly a series with respect to any one of its ordering relations, since postulate 1 does not strictly hold (see § 12 or § 74). A multiple series which is of type θ with respect to each of n serial relations is called an *n-dimensional continuum*.

An extended discussion of multiply ordered classes is contained in Cantor's memoir of 1888.*

* Cantor, *Zeitschr. f. Phil. u. philos. Kritik*, vol. 92, pp. 240–265 (1888). See also F. Riesz, *Math. Ann.*, vol. 61, pp. 406–421 (1905).

CHAPTER VII

WELL–ORDERED SERIES, WITH AN INTRODUCTION TO CANTOR'S TRANSFINITE NUMBERS

73. In §§ 21, 41, and 54, certain special kinds of series (" discrete," " dense," " continuous ") have been defined, and their chief properties discussed.

In this chapter a brief account is now to be given of another special kind of series, which has proved to be of fundamental importance in Cantor's theory of the transfinite numbers, and I hope that some readers may be led, by this brief introduction, to a further study of that most recent development of mathematical thought, in which many problems of fundamental interest still await solution.

The theory of the transfinite numbers was created by Georg Cantor in 1883, in a monograph called *Grundlagen einer allgemeinen Mannichfaltigkeitslehre; ein mathematisch-philosophischer Versuch in der Lehre des Unendlichen.* A much clearer presentation of the subject will be found in his *Beiträge zur Begründung der transfiniten Mengenlehre* in the *Mathematische Annalen* (1895, 1897) translated by P. E. B. Jourdain, *Contributions to the Founding of the Theory of Transfinite Numbers* (Open Court Pub. Co., 1915); but many of the speculations which were begun or suggested in the *Grundlagen* have not yet been developed.*

* Among the more recent treatises may be mentioned: A. Schönflies, *Entwickelung der Mengenlehre und ihrer Anwendungen,* second edition, 1913 (Teubner, Leipzig); B. Russell, *Principles of Mathematics* (1903); L. Couturat, *Les Principes des mathématiques* (1905); G. Hessenberg, *Grundbegriffe der Mengenlehre* (1906); W. H. and G. C. Young, *The Theory of Sets of Points* (1906); J. König, *Neue Grundlagen der Logik, Arithmetik und Mengenlehre* (1914); F. Hausdorff, *Grundzüge der Mengenlehre* (1914); P. E. B. Jourdain, *The Development of the Theory of Transfinite Numbers,* published serially in *Archiv der Math. u. Phys.,* ser. 3, volumes 10, 14, 16, 22 (1906–1913); and the *Principia Mathematica* by Whitehead and Russell, vol. 3 (1913).

74. A *series*, or *simply ordered class*, has been defined in § 12 as any system $(K, <)$ which satisfies the following three conditions:

POSTULATE 1. *If a and b are distinct elements of the class K, then either a < b or b < a.*

POSTULATE 2. *If a < b, then a and b are distinct.*

POSTULATE 3. *If a < b and b < c, then a < c.*

A *normal series*, or " *well-ordered* " *series (wohlgeordnete Menge),** is then any series which satisfies the following three conditions: †

---

* The earliest of Cantor's writings which bear upon this subject will be found in *Math. Ann.*, vol. 5, pp. 123–132 (1872); and in Crelle's (or Borchardt's) *Journ. für Math.*, vol. 77, pp. 258–262 (1874); vol. 84, pp. 242–258 (1877). Then came a series of six articles " Über unendliche, lineare Punktmannichfaltigkeiten," *Math. Ann.*, vol. 15, pp. 1–7 (1879); vol. 17, pp. 355–358 (1880); vol. 20, pp. 113–121 (1882); vol. 21, pp. 51–58 (1883); vol. 21, pp. 545–591 (1883); vol. 23, pp. 453–488 (1884). The fifth of these articles is identical with the monograph published in the same year (1883) under the title " Grundlagen einer allgemeinen Mannichfaltigkeitslehre " — page *n* of the " Grundlagen " corresponding to page $(n + 544)$ of the article in the *Annalen*. [All the articles mentioned thus far, or partial extracts from them, are translated into French in the *Acta Mathematica*, vol. 2, 1883. The same journal contains also some further contributions; see vol. 2, pp. 409–414 (1883); vol. 4, pp. 381–392 (1884); vol. 7, pp. 105–124 (1885).] These articles were followed by a number of writings in defence of the new theory; see especially the *Zeitschrift für Phil. und philos. Kritik*, vol. 88, pp. 224–233 (1886); vol. 91, pp. 81–125, 252–270 (1887); vol. 92, pp. 240–265 (1888). Then came a short but interesting note in the *Jahresber. d. D. Math.-Ver.*, vol. 1, pp. 75–78 (1892), and finally the " Beiträge," etc., *Math. Ann.*, vol. 46, pp. 481–512 (1895); vol. 49, pp. 207–246 (1897); French translation by F. Marotte (1899); English translation by P. E. B. Jourdain (1915). Since 1897 the literature of the subject has rapidly increased, but nothing further has been published by Cantor himself.

† G. Cantor, *Math. Ann.*, vol. 21 (1883), p. 548; *ibid.*, vol. 49 (1897), p. 207. The name " normal series " was suggested to me by the term " normally ordered class," used by E. W. Hobson as a translation of *wohlgeordnete Menge; Proc. Lond. Math. Soc.*, ser. 2, vol. 3 (1905), p. 170. It would have been a better term than " well-ordered series," for the adjective " well-ordered " applies properly only to a *class*, not to a *series*, since a series is already an *ordered class*, and a well-ordered class would be, as it were, a " well " series. But the term " well-ordered " is so well established in the literature that it seems best to retain it as the designation for this particular kind of series.

POSTULATE 4. *The series has a first element* (§ 17).

POSTULATE 5. *Every element, unless it be the last, has an immediate successor* (§ 17).

POSTULATE 6. *Every fundamental segment of the series has a limit.*

Here a "fundamental segment" is any lower segment which has no last element; the "limit" of a fundamental segment is the element next following all the elements of the segment (§§ 46, 49).

The consistency and independence of these postulates are established by the examples already given in §§ 28–29.

In a well-ordered series, any element which is the limit of a fundamental segment (and therefore has no immediate predecessor) is called a *limiting element* of the series (*Grenzelement, Element der zweiten Art*[*]). Every element which is neither a limiting element, nor the first element of the series, will have a predecessor.

For example, the series

$$1_1, 2_1, 3_1, \ldots; \quad 1_2, 2_2, 3_2, \ldots; \quad 1_3, 2_3, 3_3, \ldots; \quad \ldots; \quad 1'$$

is a well-ordered series in which the limiting elements $(1_2, 1_3, \ldots; 1')$ form a progression followed by a last element $1'$.

75. From postulates 1–6 it follows at once that Dedekind's postulate (see § 21 or § 54) will hold true in any well-ordered series; indeed *we may use Dedekind's postulate in place of postulate 6 in the definition of a well-ordered series;*[†] I prefer postulate 6 in this case, however, because it emphasizes the unsymmetrical character of the well-ordered series.

76. Other, very convenient, forms of the definition are the following:

(1) *A well-ordered series is any series in which every subclass* (§ 6) *has a first element.*[‡]

---

[*] G. Cantor, *Math. Ann.*, vol. 49 (1897), p. 226. Jourdain uses *Limes; Phil. Mag.*, ser. 6, vol. 7 (1904), p. 296. Compare § 62, above.

[†] O. Veblen, *Trans. Amer. Math. Soc.*, vol. 6 (1905), p. 170.

[‡] Cantor, *loc. cit.* (1897), p. 208.

(2) *A well-ordered series is any series which contains no subclass of the type* *ω; that is, no subclass which is a regression (§ 25).*

The equivalence of each of these definitions with the definition in § 74 is easily verified.

Examples of well-ordered series

77. The simplest examples of well-ordered series are those which contain only a finite number of elements; and since two finite series are ordinally similar when and only when they have the same number of elements, there will be a distinct type of well-ordered series corresponding to every natural number (compare § 27).

The simplest example of a well-ordered series with an infinite number of elements is a series of type ω, that is, a progression (§ 24).

78. Other examples of well-ordered series, which will serve also to explain the notation commonly used, are the following:

A progression of series each of which is itself of type ω forms a series of type ω^2:

$$1, 2, 3, \ldots \mid 1, 2, 3, \ldots \mid 1, 2, 3, \ldots \mid \ldots .$$

A progression of series each of which is of type ω^2 forms a series of type ω^3:

$$1, 2, .. \mid 1, 2, .. \mid .. \parallel 1, 2, .. \mid 1, 2, .. \mid .. \parallel 1, 2, .. \mid 2, 2, .. \mid .. \parallel \ldots .$$

So in general; a progression of series each of which is of type ω^ν forms a series of type $\omega^{\nu+1}$, where ν is any positive integer.

Any type ω^ν can be represented by a series of points on a line of length a by the following device, illustrated for the case of type ω^3.

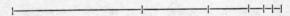

First, divide the given line into a denumerable set of intervals, as most conveniently by the set of points whose distances from the right-hand end of the line are

$$\frac{a}{2}, \ \frac{a}{4}, \ \frac{a}{8}, \ \frac{a}{16}, \ \ldots;$$

* Jourdain, *Phil. Mag.*, ser. 6, vol. 7, p. 65 (1904).

the points of division will form a series of type ω. Next, divide each interval into a denumerable set of intervals in a similar way; all the points of division taken together will form a series of type ω^2. Finally, repeating the same operation once again, we obtain a series of points of type ω^3.

79. A series of the type called ω^ω may now be constructed as follows: Take a line of length a, and divide it into a denumerable set of intervals as above; in the first of these intervals insert a series of type ω, in the second a series of type ω^2, in the third a series of type ω^3, and so on; the total collection of points thus determined forms a series of type ω^ω.

A series of type ω^ω each of whose elements is a series of type ω^ω forms a series of type $(\omega^\omega)^2$ or $\omega^{\omega \cdot 2}$.

A series of type ω^ω each of whose elements is a series of type $\omega^{\omega \cdot 2}$ forms a series of type $\omega^{\omega \cdot 3}$.

And so in general a series of type ω^ω each of whose elements is a series of type $\omega^{\omega \cdot \nu}$ forms a series of type $\omega^{\omega(\nu+1)}$.

A series of the type called ω^{ω^2} can now be constructed as follows: Divide a given line into a denumerable set of intervals as before; in the first of these intervals insert a series of type ω^ω, in the second a series of type $\omega^{\omega \cdot 2}$, in the third a series of type $\omega^{\omega \cdot 3}$, and so on; the total collection of points thus determined forms a series of type $\omega^{\omega \cdot \omega}$ or ω^{ω^2}.

A series of type ω^{ω^2} each of whose elements is a series of type ω^{ω^2} forms a series of type $(\omega^{\omega^2})^2$ or $\omega^{\omega^2 \cdot 2}$.

A series of type ω^{ω^2} each of whose elements is a series of type $\omega^{\omega^2 \cdot 2}$ forms a series of type $\omega^{\omega^2 \cdot 3}$.

And so in general a series of type $\omega^{\omega^2 \cdot \nu}$ may be constructed, and hence a series of the type $\omega^{\omega^2 \cdot \omega}$ or ω^{ω^3}, by another application of the denumerable set of intervals.

By an extension of the same methods we can thus construct series of each of the types originally denoted by $\omega_1, \omega_2, \omega_3, \ldots,$ where $\qquad \omega_1 = \omega, \quad \omega_2 = \omega^{\omega_1}, \quad \omega_3 = \omega^{\omega_2}, \quad \ldots .$[*]

---

[*] Cantor, *loc. cit.* (1897), p. 242. It should be noted that this notation has recently been abandoned, the subscripts under the ω's being now used for another purpose; see § 83.

And so on *ad infinitum;* but none of the well-ordered series thus constructed will contain more than a denumerable infinity of elements (compare § 38).

80. In order to understand one further matter of notation, consider a well-ordered series of the type represented, say, by

$$\omega^3.5 + \omega^2.7 + \omega + 2.$$

Here the plus signs indicate that the series is made up of four parts, in order from left to right; the first part consists of a series of type ω^3 taken five times in succession; the second part consists of a series of type ω^2 taken seven times in succession; the third part is a single series of type ω; and the last part is a finite series containing two elements. — And so in general the notation

$$\omega^{\mu}.\nu_0 + \omega^{\mu-1}.\nu_1 + \omega^{\mu-2}.\nu_2 + \ldots + \nu_{\mu},$$

where μ is a positive integer, and the coefficients ν_0, ν_1, ν_2, ..., ν_{μ} are positive integers or zero, is to be interpreted in a similar way.*

It will be noticed that in the case of a progression, or of any well-ordered series of the types described in §§ 78–79, the whole series is ordinally similar to each of its upper segments (§ 47); that is, if we cut off any lower segment from the series, the type is not altered. This is not true in the case of the well-ordered series of the types described in the present section.

General properties of well-ordered series

81. The fundamental properties of well-ordered series are developed very carefully and clearly in Cantor's memoir of 1897; the following theorems may be mentioned as perhaps the most important:

(1) Every subclass in a well-ordered series is itself a well-ordered series.

(2) If each element of a well-ordered series is replaced by a well-ordered series, and the whole regarded as a single series, the result will be still a well-ordered series (compare the examples in §§ 78–79).

(These two theorems follow at once from the definition in § 76, 1.)

* Cantor, *loc. cit.* (1897), p. 229.

DEFINITION. The part of a well-ordered series preceding any given element a is called a *lower segment* (*Abschnitt*) of the series (compare § 47).*

(3) A well-ordered series is never ordinally similar to any one of its lower segments, or to any part of any one of its lower segments.

(4) If two well-ordered series are ordinally similar, the ordinal correspondence between them can be set up in only one way (compare §§ 26, 45, 61, and §§ 53, 65).

(5) Any subclass of a well-ordered series is ordinally similar to the whole series or else to some one of its lower segments.

(6) If any two well-ordered series, F and G, are given, then either F is ordinally similar to G, or F is ordinally similar to some definite lower segment of G, or G is ordinally similar to some definite lower segment of F; and these three relations are mutually exclusive. In the first case, F and G are of the same type; in the second case, F is said to be *less than G;* and in the third case, G is said to be *less than F*.

82. By virtue of this theorem 6, *the various types of well-ordered series, when arranged " in the order of magnitude " (as defined in the theorem), form a series (§ 74) with respect to the relation " less than ";and, as Cantor has shown, this series is itself a well-ordered series.*

Moreover, by theorem 2, every possible collection of types of well-ordered series, arranged in order of magnitude, will be itself a well-ordered series.

Classification of the well-ordered series

83. The classification of the well-ordered series is a characteristic feature of Cantor's theory; since, however, the method of procedure, when pushed to its logical extreme, has led to controversy,

* Most writers, including Russell, translate *Abschnitt* by *segment* (without qualifying adjective); but since the word " segment " is already used in several different senses (see, for example, Veblen, *Trans. Amer. Math. Soc.*, vol. 6, p. 166, 1905), it has seemed to me safer to use the longer term " lower segment," about which there can be no ambiguity.

the whole scheme is regarded with a certain measure of suspicion.* The classification is as follows:

First, every well-ordered series in which the number of elements is finite is said to belong to the FIRST CLASS *of well-ordered series.*

Now take all the types of series belonging to the first class, and arrange them in order of magnitude (§ 82); the result is a well-ordered series of a certain type, called ω (compare § 24).

Then *every well-ordered series whose elements can be put into one-to-one correspondence (§ 3) with the elements of ω is said to belong to the* SECOND CLASS. In particular, the series of type ω are the *smallest* series of the second class.

Next, take all the types of series belonging to the second class, and arrange them in order of magnitude; the resulting series is a well-ordered series of a certain type, called ω_1 (or Ω).

* On the paradoxes of Burali-Forti, Russell, and Richard, and other questions of mathematical logic, see, for example, C. Burali-Forti, *Rend. del circ. mat. di Palermo*, vol. 11 (1897), pp. 154–164; E. Borel, *Leçons sur la théorie des fonctions* (1898), pp. 119–122, especially the second edition (1914), pp. 102–174; also a remark in *Liouville's Journ. de Math.*, ser. 5, vol. 9 (1903), p. 330; D. Hilbert, *Jahresber. d. D. Math.-Ver.*, vol. 8 (1899), p. 184; B. Russell, *Principles of Mathematics* (1903), chapter 10; E. W. Hobson, *Proc. Lond. Math. Soc.*, ser. 2, vol. 3 (1905), pp. 170–188; A. Schönflies and A. Korselt, *Jahresber. d. D. Math.-Ver.*, vol. 15 (1906), pp. 19–25 and 215–219; P. E. B. Jourdain and G. Peano, *Rivista di Matematica*, vol. 8 (1906), pp. 121–136 and 136–157; G. H. Hardy, A. C. Dixon, E. W. Hobson, B. Russell, P. E. B. Jourdain, and A. C. Dixon, *Proc. Lond. Math. Soc.*, ser. 2, vol. 4 (1906), pp. 10–17, 18–20, 21–28, 29–53, 266–283, and 317–319; B. Russell, *Rev. de Métaphys. et de Mor.*, vol. 14 (1906), pp. 627–650; J. Richard, *Acta Mathematica*, vol. 30 (1906), pp. 295–296, and *Ens. Math.*, vol. 9 (1907), pp. 94–98; E. B. Wilson, *Bull. Amer. Math. Soc.*, vol. 14 (1908), pp. 432–443; A. Schönflies, E. Zermelo, and H. Poincaré, *Acta Mathematica*, vol. 32 (1909), pp. 177–184, 185–193, and 195–200; A. Koyré and B. Russell, *Rev. de Métaphys. et de Mor.*, vol. 20 (1912), pp. 722–724 and 725–726; H. Dingler, *Jahresber. d. D. Math.-Ver.*, vol. 22 (1913), pp. 307–315; N. Wiener, *Messenger of Mathematics*, vol. 43 (1913), pp. 97–105; a curious paper by H. Glause, *Rend. del circ. mat. di Palermo*, vol. 38 (1914), pp. 324–329; and the recent treatises by Schönflies, König, and Hausdorff, cited in a footnote to § 73; especially Whitehead and Russell, *Principia Mathematica*, vol. 1 (1910), pp. 63–68. On the controversy especially connected with Zermelo's "multiplicative axiom," see the references under § 84. On the problem of consistency see references under § 19.

Then *every well-ordered series whose elements can be put into one-to-one correspondence with the elements of* ω_1 *is said to belong to the* THIRD CLASS. In particular, the series of type ω_1 are the *smallest* series of the third class.

And so on. In general, *every well-ordered series whose elements can be put into one-to-one correspondence with the elements of* ω_ν (where ν is any positive integer) *is said to belong to the* $(\nu + 2)$th CLASS; and the series of type ω_ν will be the *smallest* series of that class.*

Moreover, by an extension of the device already employed several times, we can define a class of well-ordered series whose smallest type would be denoted by ω_ω, or even ω_{ω_1}; and so on, *ad infinitum*; so that when we speak of the nth class of well-ordered series, n need not be a positive integer, but may itself denote the type of any well ordered series.

84. In order to justify this classification, it is necessary to show that the classes described are really all distinct, so that no well-ordered series belongs to more than one class; and further, that well-ordered series belonging to each class actually exist, so that no class is " empty." Cantor has completed this investigation only as far as the first and second classes; each of the examples mentioned above is a well-ordered series of the first or second class (since the number of elements in each case is at most denumerable, in view of § 38); no similar example of a series of even the third class has yet been satisfactorily constructed.† Problems concerning

---

* The notation ω_ν for the smallest type of the $(\nu + 2)$th class was introduced by Russell, *Principles of Mathematics*, vol. 1 (1903), p. 322; compare Jourdain, *Phil. Mag.*, ser. 6, vol. 7 (1904), p. 295. The symbols ω and Ω were first used in this connection by Cantor in *Math. Ann.*, vol. 21, pp. 577, 582 (1883).

† The question whether every class can be arranged as a well-ordered series, was first proposed by Cantor in 1883 (*Math. Ann.*, vol. 21, p. 550). The controversy centers about two papers by E. Zermelo; *Beweis dass jede Menge wohlgeordnet werden kann*, Math. Ann., vol. 59 (1904), pp. 514–516; *Neuer Beweis für die Möglichkeit einer Wohlordnung*, Math. Ann., vol. 65 (1907), pp. 107–128. See, for example, J. König, A. Schönflies, F. Bernstein, E. Borel, and P. E. B. Jourdain, *Math. Ann.*, vol. 60 (1905), pp. 177, 181, 187, 194, 465; J. Hadamard, R. Baire, H. Lebesgue, and E. Borel, *Bull. de la Soc. Math. de*

the existence of the higher classes, and the question whether every collection can be arranged as a well-ordered series, are still being actively debated (see § 89).

85. The various classes of well-ordered series can also be defined by purely ordinal postulates, as Veblen has shown how to do in his recent memoir.*

Thus, a well-ordered series of the *first class* is any well-ordered series which satisfies not only the postulates 1–6 of § 74, but also the further conditions 7_1 and 8_1, namely:

POSTULATE 7_1. *Every element except the first has a predecessor* (§ 17).

POSTULATE 8_1. *There is a last element* (§ 17).

The *type* ω is then defined by postulates 1–6 with 7_1 and $8'_1$, where $8'_1$, is the contradictory of 8_1:

POSTULATE $8'_1$. *There is no last element.*

Next, a well-ordered series of the *second class* is any well-ordered series, not of the first class, which satisfies 7_2 and 8_2, namely:

POSTULATE 7_2. *Every element except the first either has a predecessor or is the upper limit of some subclass of type ω* (*as just defined*).

POSTULATE 8_2. *There is either a last element, or a subclass of type ω which surpasses any given element of the series.†*

The *type* ω_1 (or Ω) is then defined by postulates 1–6 with 7_2 and $8'_2$, where $8'_2$ is the contradictory of 8_2.

POSTULATE $8'_2$. *There is no last element; and every subclass of type ω has an upper limit in the series.*

France, vol. 33 (1905), pp. 261–273; G. Peano, *Rivista di Matematica*, vol. 8 (1906), p. 145; J. König, *Math. Ann.*, vol. 61 (1905), pp. 156–160, and vol. 63 (1906), pp. 217–221; H. Poincaré, *Rev. de Métaphys. et de Mor.*, vol. 14 (1906), pp. 294–317; H. Lebesgue, *Bull. de la Soc. Math. de France*, vol. 35 (1907), pp. 202–212; G. Vivanti, *Rend. del circ. mat. di Palermo*, vol. 25 (1908), pp. 205–208; G. Hessenberg, *Crelle's Journ. für Math.*, vol. 135 (1908), pp. 81–133, 318; E. Zermelo, *Math. Ann.*, vol. 65 (1908), pp. 261–281; and the recent treatises by Schönflies, König, and Hausdorff cited in a footnote to § 73, especially Whitehead and Russell, *Principia Mathematica*, vol. 3 (1913), p. 3. For a third proof by F. Hartogs (1915), see § 89*a*.

* O. Veblen, *Trans. Amer. Math. Soc.*, vol. 6, p. 170 (1905).

† That is, if x is any element of the given series, there is an element y in the subclass for which $x < y$.

Similarly, a well-ordered series of the *third class* is any well-ordered series, not of the first or second class, which satisfies 7_3 and 8_3, namely:

POSTULATE 7_3. *Every element except the first either has a predecessor, or is the upper limit of some subclass of type ω, or is the upper limit of some subclass of type ω₁.*

POSTULATE 8_3. *There is either a last element, or a subclass of type ω which surpasses any given element, or a subclass of type ω₁ which surpasses any given element.*

The *type ω₂* is then defined by postulates 1–6 with 7_3 and $8'_3$, where, as before, $8'_3$ denotes the contradictory of 8_3:

POSTULATE $8'_3$. *There is no last element; every subclass of type ω has an upper limit in the series; and every subclass of type ω₁ has an upper limit in the series.*

And so on. The establishment of definite sets of postulates like these seems to me an essential step toward the solution of the difficult problems connected with this subject. For example, Cantor's proof that a series of type Ω is non-denumerable is simply a demonstration that no denumerable series can satisfy the eight postulates here numbered 1–6, 7_2, and $8'_2$.

The transfinite ordinal numbers

86. It is now easy to explain what is meant by the *ordinal numbers (Ordnungszahlen)*, in the generalized sense in which Cantor now uses that term: *they are simply the various types of order exhibited by the well-ordered series.*[*] In other words, according to the theory of Russell, the ordinal number corresponding to any given well-ordered series is the *class of all series which are ordinally similar to the given series;* any one of these ordinally similar series may be taken to represent the ordinal number of the given series.[†]

The ordinal numbers of the *first class* (§ 83) are the *finite* ordinal numbers, with which we have always been familiar; the ordinal

---

[*] Cantor, *Zeitschrift für Philos. und philos. Kritik*, vol. 91 (1887), p. 84; and *Math. Ann.*, vol. 49 (1897), p. 216.

[†] Russell, *Principles of Mathematics*, vol. 1 (1903), p. 312.

numbers of the *second or higher classes* are the *transfinite* ordinal numbers created by Cantor, which constitute, in a certain true sense, " *eine Fortsetzung der realen ganzen Zahlenreihe über das Unendliche hinaus.*" *

The smallest of the transfinite ordinals is ω.

By the *sum*, $a + b$, of two ordinal numbers, a and b, is meant simply the type of series obtained when a series of type a is followed by a series of type b and the whole regarded as a single series.†
Clearly $a + b$ will not always be the same as $b + a$ (for example, $1 + \omega = \omega$, while $\omega + 1$ is a new type); but always $(a + b) + c = a + (b + c)$.

By the *product*, ab, of an ordinal number a multiplied by an ordinal number b, is meant the type of series obtained as follows: in a series of type b replace each element by a series of type a, and regard the whole as a single series; the result will be a well-ordered series (by § 81, 2), and the type of this well-ordered series is what is meant by ab.‡ Clearly ab will not always equal ba (for example, $2\omega = \omega$, while $\omega.2$ is a new type); but always $(ab)c = a(bc)$, and also $a(b + c) = ab + ac$, although not $(b + c)a = ba + ca$.

The definition of a^b, where a and b are general ordinal numbers is too complicated to repeat in this place.§ Enough has at any rate been said to give at least some notion of the nature of the artificial algebra which Cantor has here so ingeniously constructed.

The transfinite cardinal numbers

87. For the sake of completeness I add here a brief note on the meaning of some of the terms in Cantor's theory of the (generalized) cardinal numbers.‖ This theory has nothing to do with series, or *ordered* classes, but is a development of the theory of *classes as such* (§ 11); nevertheless the difficulties met with in this theory are closely analogous to the difficulties we have pointed out

* *Math. Ann.*, vol. 21 (1883), p. 545.

† *Math. Ann.*, vol. 21 (1883), p. 550.

‡ In Cantor's earlier definition of the product ab, a was the multiplier (*loc. cit.*, 1883, p. 551); the order was changed in his later articles, so that a is now the multiplicand (see *loc. cit.*, 1887, p. 96, and 1897, pp. 217, 231).

§ Cantor, *Math. Ann.*, vol. 49 (1897), p. 231; Hausdorff, *loc. cit.* (1914), p. 147.

‖ The standard account of this theory is in Cantor's article of 1895.

in the theory of the ordinal numbers (§ 84), and it is impossible to read the literature of either theory without some acquaintance with the other.

88. If two classes can be brought into one-to-one correspondence (§ 3), they are said to be *equivalent* (*äquivalent*). For example, the class of rational numbers is equivalent to the class of positive integers (compare § 19, 6); or the class of points on a line is equivalent to the class of all points in space (§ 71).

The *cardinal number* (*Mächtigkeit*) of a given class A is then defined as *the class of all those classes which are equivalent to A.** The *finite* cardinal numbers are the cardinal numbers which belong to finite classes; the *transfinite* cardinals are those which belong to infinite classes (§ 7).

According to this definition, if two classes A and B are *equivalent*, their cardinal numbers will clearly be *identical*.

If a class A is equivalent to a part of a class B, but not to the whole, then A is said to be *less than B;* in this case the cardinal number of A will be *less than* the cardinal number of B.

We cannot, however, affirm that all cardinal numbers can be arranged as a series, in order of magnitude, for while postulates 2 and 3 (§ 74) clearly hold with regard to the relation "less than" as just defined, postulate 1, which may be called the *principle of comparison* (*Vergleichbarkeit*) for classes, has never been proved. In other words, non-equivalent classes may possibly exist, neither of which is " less than " the other; but see § 89a.†

On the other hand, Cantor has proved that when any class is given, a class can be constructed which shall have a greater cardinal number than the given class.‡

---

* The term *Mächtigkeit* was first used by Cantor in *Crelle's Journ. für Math.*, vol. 84, p. 242 (1877). Power, potency, multitude, and dignity are some of the English equivalents. The term *Cardinalzahl* was introduced in 1887. Cf. Cantor, *loc. cit.* (1887), pp. 84 and 118. The notion of a cardinal number as a *class* is emphasized by Russell; *Principle of Mathematics*, vol. 1 (1903), p. 312.

† Compare E. Borel, *Leçons sur la théorie des fonctions* (1898), pp. 102–110.

‡ Cantor, *J. d. D. Math.-Ver.*, vol. 1 (1892), p. 77; E. Borel, *loc. cit.* (1898), p. 107; C. S. Peirce, *Monist*, vol. 16 (1906), pp. 497–502.

For example, let C denote the class of elements in a linear continuum, say the class of points on a line one inch long (compare § 71); and let C' denote the class of all possible " bi-colored rods " which can be constructed by painting each point of the given line either red or blue. Then the class of rods, C', has a higher cardinal number than the class of points, C, as may be proved as follows:

In the first place, *C is equivalent to a part of C';* for example, to the class of rods in which one point is painted red and all the other points blue. Secondly, *C is not equivalent to the whole of C';* for, if any alleged one-to-one correspondence between the rods and the points were proposed, we could at once define a rod which would not be included in the scheme: namely, the rod in which the color of each point x is opposite to the color of the point x in the rod which is assigned to the point x of the given line; this rod would differ from each rod of the proposed scheme in the color of at least one point. (Cf. § 40.)

The class C' has therefore a higher cardinal number than the class C. It is not known, however, whether there may not be other classes whose cardinal numbers lie between the cardinal numbers of C and C'.

89. Of special interest are the cardinal numbers of the various types of well-ordered series; but when we speak of the cardinal number of a *series*, it must be understood that we mean the cardinal number of the *class of elements which occur in the series*, without regard to their order.

The cardinal numbers of the finite well-ordered series are the *finite cardinal numbers*, with which we have always been familiar.

The cardinal number of a series of type ω (§ 24) is denoted by the Hebrew letter Aleph with a subscript 0:[*]

$$\aleph_0.$$

This $\aleph_0$ will then be the cardinal number of any well-ordered series of the second class (§ 83), since all the series of the second class are, by definition, equivalent.

The cardinal number of a series of type ω_1 (or Ω) is denoted by $\aleph_1$; this will then be the cardinal number of any well-ordered series of the third class.

* Cantor, *Math. Ann.*, vol. 46 (1895), p. 492.

And so on. In general, the cardinal number of a series of type ω_ν is denoted by $\aleph_\nu$; this will then be the cardinal number of any well-ordered series of the $(\nu + 2)$th class.

If we assume the series of classes of ordinal numbers (§ 84), we thus obtain a series of cardinal numbers

$$\aleph_1, \aleph_1, \ldots, \aleph_\omega, \ldots,$$

arranged in order of increasing magnitude; this series will be a well-ordered series with respect to the relation " less than," and ordinally similar to the series of ordinal numbers; but all the difficulties that are involved in the one series are involved in the other. In particular, it requires proof to show that two Alephs, as $\aleph_\nu$ and $\aleph_{\nu+1}$, are really non-equivalent, and that no other cardinal number lies between them. Cantor has shown merely that $\aleph_0$ is the *smallest* transfinite cardinal number, and that $\aleph_1$ is the number *next greater*.[*] Again, the vexed question: *can the cardinal number of the linear continuum* (§ 54) *be found among the Alephs ?* is equivalent to the question: *can the class of elements in the continuum be arranged in the form of a well-ordered series ?* (See § 89a.) It is usually supposed that the cardinal number of the continuum will prove to be $\aleph_1$.

89a. In this section we reproduce, in brief outline, Hartogs's recent proof of Zermelo's theorem that *every class can be arranged as a well-ordered series.*[†]

Let there be given any non-empty class, M.

First, consider all possible well-ordered series, $G, H, \ldots,$ whose elements belong to M, and let N be the class composed of these series, together with the null series, 0.

Next, within this class N, group together all the well-ordered series $G', G'', \ldots$ which are similar to G into a subclass, g; group together all the well-ordered series $H', H'', \ldots$ which are similar to H into a subclass, h; etc.

These subclasses, $g, h, \ldots$ (one of which is the null class) are now to form the elements of a series, L, whose rule of order is the following: A subclass g is said to precede a subclass h $(g \prec h)$, if

[*] *Math. Ann.*, vol. 21, p. 581 (1883).

[†] F. Hartogs, *Über das Problem der Wohlordnung, Math. Ann.*, vol. 76 (1915), pp. 438–443.

any one of the well-ordered series belonging to g is similar to a lower segment of any one of the well-ordered series H belonging to h. (It is clear that it makes no difference which G is taken from g, or which H is taken from h, etc., since all the G's in g are similar to each other, and all the H's in h are similar to each other, etc.) From this definition it follows that if any two of the subclasses, say g and h, are distinct, then either $g \prec h$ or else $h \prec g$, and not both; also that if g, h, i are three subclasses such that $g \prec h$ and $h \prec i$, then $g \prec i$. In other words, the subclasses g, h, . . . form a series, L, with respect to the rule of order stated.

Moreover, *the series L thus constructed is a well-ordered series.* The proof is as follows: Let g be any element of L, and let G be any one of the well-ordered series belonging to g. Then the elements of L which precede g stand in a one-to-one correspondence (preserving order) with the lower segments of G. But the lower segments of G form a well-ordered series; hence, no matter what element g may be chosen, the elements of L preceding g form a well-ordered series. From this it follows that the series L itself must be well-ordered. For, if L were not well-ordered, it would contain at least one regression, r (§ 76), so that if g is any element of r, then the elements of r preceding g would form a series having no first element; but this is impossible, since the elements of r preceding g are part of the elements of L preceding g, and hence are part of a well-ordered series, and as such must have a first element. The whole series L is therefore a well-ordered series.

Further, each of the well-ordered series G, H, . . . which can be formed out of elements of M, is similar to some lower segment of L. In particular, the well-ordered series G is similar to that lower segment of L which is determined by the subclass g to which G belongs. For, as we have just noted, there is a one-to-one correspondence (preserving order) between the subclasses that precede g and the lower segments of G, and there is also a one-to-one correspondence (preserving order) between the lower segments of G and the elements of G.

Considering now the elements of L, without regard to their order, we see at once that *the elements of L cannot be placed in one-to-one correspondence with the elements of M, nor with the elements of any part of M.* For, suppose the contrary; then M, or some part of M, would be capable of being well-ordered, so that we should have a well-ordered series, formed out of elements of M, and similar to L; but this is impossible, since we have proved that every such well-ordered series is similar to some lower segment of L, and no lower segment of L can be similar to L itself.

Finally, if we assume the principle of comparison between classes (§ 88), there is only one alternative left, namely: *it must be possible to place the elements of M in one-to-one correspondence with the elements of a part of L.* But since L is well-ordered, every part of L is well-ordered; hence we have the theorem that whatever class M may be, its elements can always be so arranged as to form a well-ordered series.[*]

90. We speak next of the sums and products of the cardinal numbers.[†]

The *sum $A + B$* of two classes A and B which have no common element is the class containing all the elements of A and B together.

If a and b are the cardinal numbers of two such classes A and B, the *sum*, $a + b$, of these two cardinals is then defined as the cardinal number of $A + B$. Clearly $a + b = b + a$, and $(a + b) + c = a + (b + c)$.

The *product*, AB, of two classes A and B which have no common element is the class of all couples (a, β), where a is any element of A, and β any element of B.

If a and b are the cardinal numbers of two such classes, the *product*, ab, of these two cardinals is then defined as the cardinal number of AB. Clearly, $ab = ba$, $(ab)c = a(bc)$, and $a(b + c) = ab + ac$.

Finally, A^B denotes the class of all *coverings* (*Belegungen*) of B by A, where a " covering " of B by A is any law according to which each element of B determines uniquely an element of A (not excluding the cases in which various elements of B may determine the same element of A).[‡]

The *b^{th} power of a*, a^b, where a and b are the cardinal numbers of any two classes A and B, is then defined as the cardinal number of A^B. Clearly $a^b a^c = a^{b+c}$, $(a^b)^c = a^{bc}$, and $(ab)^c = a^c b^c$.

In this way Cantor has constructed an artificial algebra of the cardinal numbers, analogous to the algebra of the ordinal numbers,

---

[*] Hartogs's paper shows that the following three principles are equivalent: (1) the principle of comparison between classes; (2) the principle that every class can be well-ordered; and (3) the much discussed "multiplicative axiom" of Zermelo. See references under § 84, especially Whitehead and Russell, *Principia Mathematica*, vol. 1 (1910), p. 561.

[†] *Zeitschr. f. Phil. u. philos. Kritik*, vol. 91 (1887), pp. 120–121; *Math. Ann.*, vol. 46 (1895), p. 485.

[‡] *Math. Ann.*, vol. 46 (1895), p. 487.

but resembling much more closely the familiar algebra of the finite integers.

Perhaps the most famous result obtained in this algebra is the formula*

$$c = 2^{\aleph_0},$$

where c stands for the cardinal number of the continuum, and $2^{\aleph_0}$ is determined according to the rule just stated for the powers of cardinal numbers. It becomes an important question, therefore, to decide whether

$$2^{\aleph_0} = \aleph_1$$

or not (compare § 89, end).

91. In conclusion, it may be well to repeat that when we speak of a *cardinal* number, we always mean the cardinal number *of some given class;* and when we speak of an *ordinal* number, we always mean the ordinal number *of some given well-ordered series.*

Whether these new concepts will find important applications in practical problems is a question for the future to decide. (The *elementary* parts of Cantor's work have already proved useful, indeed almost indispensable, in the theory of functions of a real variable.†)

* *Math. Ann.*, vol. 46 (1895), p. 488.

† See, for example, R. Baire, *Leçons sur les fonctions discontinues* (1905); E. Borel, *Leçons sur la théorie des fonctions*, 2nd edit. (1914); E. W. Hobson, *Theory of Functions of a Real Variable* (1907); J. Pierpont, *Lectures on the Theory of Functions of a Real Variable* (1905, 1912); etc.; also the treatises cited under § 73.

INDEX OF TECHNICAL TERMS

The principal bibliographical footnotes will be found under the introduction, and
under §§ 73–74, and §§ 83–84.

Alephs, § 89.

Between, § 17.
Binary fractions, § 30.
Bound (upper and lower), § 56.

Cardinal numbers, § 88.
Class, § 1. (See empty, null, finite,
infinite, denumerable, simply and
multiply ordered, well-ordered,
equivalent.)
Classes of transfinites, §§ 86, 89.
Closed (series), § 62.
—— (set of points), § 62a.
Cluster point, § 62a.
Compact (series), § 41.
—— (set of points), § 62a.
Comparison (of classes), § 88.
Consistency (of postulates), § 19.
Continued fractions, § 71.
Continuous (series), §§ 54, 62, 67.
Continuum, §§ 61, 72.
—— problem, § 89.
Correspondence (of classes), § 3.
—— (of series), § 16.
Covering, § 90.

Decimal fraction, §§ 19 (9), 40, 63 (4).
Dedekind's postulate, §§ 21, 54, 75.
Dense (series), §§ 41, 54, 62.
—— (set of points), § 62a.
Dense-in-itself (series), § 62.
—— (set of points), § 62a.

Denumerable (class), § 37.
—— (series), § 41.
Derived set, § 62a.
Digits, § 30.
Dimensionality, §§ 67–71.
Discrete (series), §§ 21, 26.
Distinct (elements), § 2.

Element (of a class), § 1. (See distinct, equal, first, last, rational,
irrational, principal, limit.)
Empty (class), § 1.
Equal (elements), § 2.
Equivalent (classes), § 88.

Finite (classes), §§ 7, 27.
—— (series), § 27.
—— (numbers), §§ 86, 88.
First (element of a series), § 17.
Fraction, § 19. (See proper, decimal,
binary, ternary, continued.)
Framework (of a series), §§ 59, 67.
Fundamental (segment), § 46.
—— (sequence), § 62.

Independence (of postulates), § 20.
Induction, § 23.
Infinite (classes), §§ 7, 27.
—— (numbers), §§ 86, 88.
Integral (numbers), §§ 22, 34, 63 (3).
Irrational (elements), § 59.
—— (numbers), § 63 (3).

81

CONTRIBUTIONS TO THE FOUNDIING OF THE THEORY OF TRANSFINITE NUMBERS
by Georg Cantor

One of the greatest mathematical classics of all time, this work established a new field of mathematics of incalculable importance in topology, number theory, analysis, theory of functions, etc., as well as the entire field of modern logic. It is one of the few advanced mathematical expositions which is sufficiently fundamental so that nearly anyone with a good grasp of college mathematics can understand most of the basic ideas and many of the demonstrations. In clarity of thought and exposition it has never been surpassed; each new concept is set forth and analyzed with precision and lucidity and the systematic development of the new mathematics is logically impeccable.

Cantor first develops the elementary definitions and operations of cardinal and ordinal numbers and analyzes the concepts of "cardinality" and "ordinality." He covers such topics as the addition, multiplication, and exponentiation of cardinal numbers, the smallest transfinite cardinal number, the ordinal types of simply ordered aggregates, operations on ordinal types, the ordinal type of the linear continuum, and others. He then develops a theory of well-ordered aggregates, and investigates the ordinal numbers of well-ordered aggregates and the properties and extent of the transfinite ordinal numbers.

An 82 page Introduction by the eminent mathematical historian Philip E. B. Joudain, covers the steps by which Cantor developed the theory of transfinite numbers, the work of such predecessors as Weierstrass, Cauchy, Dedekind, Dirichlet, Riemann, Fourier, and Hankel, and Cantor's influence on such men as Frege, Peano, Whitehead, Russell, Ramsey, etc.

"Would serve as well as any modern text to initiate a student in this exciting branch of mathematics," MATHEMATICAL GAZETTE.

Bibliographic appendix to 1915. Index. ix + 211pp. 5⅜ x 8.

S45 Paperbound $1.25

A TREATISE ON ADVANCED TRIGONOMETRY
by E. W. Hobson

This reprint of Hobson's classic formerly entitled A TREATISE ON PLANE TRIGONOMETRY, will be appreciated by the mathematician, the engineer, the mathematics instructor and everybody interested in a formal exposition of trigonometry and the related topics of complex variables and infinite series. Historically of great importance, this work continues to provide much stimulating and valuable material not easily obtainable elsewhere. One of the few books on advanced trigonometry, it goes far beyond the usual college level. It is the most complete analytic treatment of the subject available in English. The variety of trigonometric relations, is unusually wide and complete. A wealth of problems and formulae, fully worked out, is found throughout the body of the book and hundreds of additional examples are given in special sections.

Partial contents. CIRCULAR FUNCTIONS: GENERAL, OF 2 OR MORE ANGLES, OF SUBMULTIPLE ANGLES. Identities & transformations, solution of equations, maximan & minima, porismatic systems of equations, summation of series. EXPANSION OF FUNCTIONS OF MULTIPLE ANGLES. Series in descending, ascending powers of sine or cosine. Euler's product. Relation between trigonometrical & algrebraic identities. TRIGONOMETRICAL TABLES. RELATIONS BETWEEN SIDES & ANGLES OF A TRIANGLE. SOLUTION OF TRIANGLE. PROPERTIES OF TRIANGLES & QUADRILATERALS. Medians, bisectos of angles, pedal triangle. COMPLEX NUMBERS: geometrical representation, powers, de Moivre's theorem, factorization, etc. THEORY OF INFINITE SERIES. Convergence of real and complex series, continuous functions, uniform convergence, geometrical series, etc. EXPONENTIAL FUNCTION, LOGARITHMS. Exponential series, generalized logarithms, Gregory's series, summation of series. HYPERBOLIC SERIES. Solution of cubic equations, table of Godermannian functions. INFINITE PRODUCTS. Convergence of infinite products, series for tangent, cotangent, secant, cosecant, etc. CONTINUED FRACTIONS: proof of irrationality of pi, Euler's transformations, etc.

Many problems are solved completely in the text. 689 examples, at chapter ends. 66 figures. xvi + 383pp. 5⅜ x 8.

S353 Paperbound **$1.95**

TABLES OF FUNCTIONS WITH FORMULAE AND CURVES

by Eugene Jahnke and Fritz Emde

This new edition of Jahnke and Emde's TABLES OF FUNCTIONS contains corrections of 396 tabular errors detected in the preceding edition, and a supplementary bibliography of 43 titles. Also added is an exhaustive 76-page appendix of tables and formulae of elementary functions. This appendix does not appear in other American editions of Jahnke and Emde. Hundreds of reliefs of functions give a helpful picture of functional relations.

PARTIAL CONTENTS. 1. Sine, cosine, and logarithmic integral. 2. Factorial function. 3. Error integral and related functions. 4. Theta-functions. 5. Elliptic integrals. 6. Elliptic functions. 7. Legendre functions. 8. Bessel functions. 9. The Riemann-Zeta function. 10. Confluent hypergeometric functions. 11. Mathieu functions. 12. Some often used constants. 13. Table of powers. 14. Auxiliary tables for computation with complex numbers. 15. Cubic equations. 16. Elementary transcendental equations. 17. Exponential function. 18. Planck's radiation function. 19. Source functions of heat conduction. 20. The hyperbolic functions. 21. Circular and hyperbolic functions of a complex variable. Bibliography and supplementary bibliography. Indexed.

Fourth revised edition. 212 figures. 400pp. (Text in both English and German.) 5⅜ x 8.

"There is hardly any single volume which could be more useful to the general applied mathematician and the mathematical physicist than this remarkable work of Jahnke and Emde," BULLETIN, NATIONAL RESEARCH COUNCIL.

"Most physicists probably know the tables of Jahnke and Emde, in which many of us look for those out-of-the-way functions for which we know no other source," SCIENTIFIC COMPUTING SERVICE LTD.

S133 Paperbound **$2.00**

THEORY OF SETS
by E. Kamke

This is the clearest and simplest introduction to the theory of sets. Making use of the discoveries of such mathematicians as Cantor, Russell, Weierstrass, Zermelo, Bernstein, Dedekind, and others, it analyzes the concepts and principles of set theory. Although emphasis is on fundamentals, special subdivisions, such as the theory of sets of points, are considered. The text is accompanied by innumerable examples. Presentation is simple, easily comprehensible to a reader who has some acquaintance with college algebra.

"Exceptionally well written," **SCHOOL SCIENCE AND MATHEMATICS.** "A very fine book," **MATHEMATICS TEACHER.** "Of real service to logicians and philosophers who have hitherto had no access to a concise and accurate introduction to the general theory of sets," **PHILOSOPHICAL REVIEW.**

PARTIAL CONTENTS. I. RUDIMENTS OF SET THEORY. First classifications, subsets, sums, intersection of sets, nonenumerable sets, etc. II. ARBITRARY SETS AND THEIR CARDINAL NUMBERS. Extensions of number concept; equivalence of sets; cardinal numbers; Bernstein's theorem; sums, products of two, many cardinal numbers; powers, etc. III. ORDERED SETS AND THEIR ORDER TYPES. Definition; similarity; order type; sum, product of order types; powers, dense sets, continuous sets, etc. IV. WELL-ORDERED SETS AND THEIR ORDINAL NUMBERS. Definition of well-ordering, ordinal numbers; addition, multiplication of ordinal numbers; subsets, similarity mappings; comparison of ordinal numbers, sequences or ordinals, operations with ordinals; transfinite induction; products, powers of ordinal numbers; well-ordering theorem; well-ordering of cardinal numbers, ordinal numbers and sets of points, and similar topics.

Translated from the second edition by Frederick Bagemihl. Bibliography. Key to symbols used. Index. vii + 144pp. 5⅜ x 8.

S141 Paperbound **$1.35**

INFINITE SEQUENCES AND SERIES
by Konrad Knopp

One of the best expositors in the field of modern mathematics, Dr. Konrad Knopp here concentrates upon two topics that are of particular interest to 20th century mathematicians. He develops the theory of infinite sequences and series from its beginnings to a point where the reader will be in a suitable position to investigate more advanced stages on his own initiative. The foundations of the theory are therefore presented with especial care, while developmental aspects are limited to the scope and purpose of the book.

All definitions are clearly stated; all theorems are proved with enough detail to make them readily comprehensible. In Chapter 1, the author begins with the construction of the system of real and complex numbers, and proceeds through such fundamental concepts as sets of numbers, and functions of real and complex variables. In his treatment of Sequences and Series (Chapter 2), he covers arbitrary and null sequences; sequences and sets of of numbers; convergence, divergence; Cauchy's limit theorem; main tests for sequences; and infinite series. Chapter 3 deals with main tests for infinite series, and operating with convergent series. Chapters 4 and 5 explain power series and the development of the theory of convergence, respectively. Chapter 6 treats expansion of the elementary functions; and Chapter 7 concludes with numerical and closed evaluation of series.

Translated by Frederick Bagemihl. Bibliography. Index. 186pp. 5⅜ x 8.

DOVER BOOKS ON SCIENCE
BOOKS THAT EXPLAIN SCIENCE

CONCERNING THE NATURE OF THINGS, Sir William Bragg. Christmas lectures delivered at the Royal Society by Nobel laureate. Why a spinning ball travels in a curved track; how uranium is transmuted to lead, etc. Partial contents: atoms, gases, liquids, crystals, metals etc. No scientific background needed; wonderful for intelligent high school student. 32pp. of photos, 57 figures. xii + 232pp. 5⅜ x 8. **T31 Paperbound $1.35**

THE NATURE OF LIGHT AND COLOUR IN THE OPEN AIR, M. Minnaert. Why is falling snow sometimes black? What causes mirages, the fata morgana, multiple suns and moons in the sky; how are shadows formed? Prof. Minnaert of the University of Utrecht answers these and similar questions in optics, light, colour, for non-specialists. Particularly valuable to nature, science students, painters, photographers. Translated by H. M. Kremer-Priest, K. Jay. 202 illustrations, including 42 photos. xvi + 362pp. 5⅜ x 8. **T196 Paperbound $1.95**

THE RESTLESS UNIVERSE, Max Born. New enlarged version of this remarkably readable account by a Noble laureate. Moving from subatomic particles to universe, the author explains in very simple terms the latest theories of wave mechanics. Partial contents: air and its relatives, electrons & ions, waves & particles, electronic structure of the atom, nuclear physics. Nearly 600 illustrations, including 7 animated sequences. 325pp. 6 x 9. **T412 Paperbound $2.00**

MATTER & LIGHT, THE NEW PHYSICS, L. de Broglie. Non-technical papers by a Nobel laureate explain electromagnetic theory, relativity, matter, light and radiation, wave mechanics, quantum physics, philosophy of science. Einstein, Planck, Bohr, others explained so easily that no mathematical training is needed for all but 2 of the 21 chapters. Unabridged. Index. 300pp. 5⅜ x 8. **T35 Paperbound $1.75**

THE COMMON SENSE OF THE EXACT SCIENCES, W. K. Clifford. Introduction by James Newman, edited by Karl Pearson. For 70 years this has been a guide to classical scientific and mathematical thought. Explains with unusual clarity basic concepts, such as extension of meaning of symbols, characteristics of surface boundaries, properties of plane figures, vectors, Cartesian method of determining position, etc. Long preface by Bertrand Russell. Bibliography of Clifford. Corrected, 130 diagrams redrawn. 249pp. 5⅜ x 8. **T61 Paperbound $1.60**

THE EVOLUTION OF SCIENTIFIC THOUGHT FROM NEWTON TO EINSTEIN, A. d'Abro. Einstein's special and general theories of relativity, with their historical implications, are analyzed in non-technical terms. Excellent accounts of the contributions of Newton, Riemann, Weyl, Planck, Eddington, Maxwell, Lorentz and others are treated in terms of space and time, equations of electromagnetics, finiteness of the universe, methodology of science. 21 diagrams. 482pp. 5⅜ x 8. **T2 Paperbound $2.00**

WHAT IS SCIENCE, Norman Campbell. This excellent introduction explains scientific method, role of mathematics, types of scientific laws. Contents: 2 aspects of science, science & nature, laws of science, discovery of laws, explanation of laws, measurement & numerical laws, applications of science. 192pp. 5⅜ x 8. **S43 Paperbound $1.25**

THE RISE OF THE NEW PHYSICS, A. d'Abro. A half-million word exposition, formerly titled THE DECLINE OF MECHANISM, for readers not versed in higher mathematics. The only thorough explanation, in everyday language, of the central core of modern mathematical physical theory, treating both classical and modern theoretical physics, and presenting in terms almost anyone can understand the equivalent of 5 years of study of mathematical physics. Scientifically impeccable coverage of mathematical-physical thought from the Newtonian system up through the electronic theories of Dirac and Heisenberg and Fermi's statistics. Combines both history and exposition; provides a broad yet unified and detailed view, with constant comparison of classical and modern views on phenomena and theories. "A must for anyone doing serious study in the physical sciences," **JOURNAL OF THE FRANKLIN INSTITUTE.** "Extraordinary faculty . . . to explain ideas and theories of theoretical physics in the language of daily life," **ISIS.** Indexed. 97 illustrations. ix + 982pp. 5⅜ x 8.
T3 Volume 1, Paperbound $2.00
T4 Volume 2, Paperbound $2.00

A HISTORY OF ASTRONOMY FROM THALES TO KEPLER, J. L. E. Dreyer. (Formerly A HISTORY OF PLANETARY SYSTEMS FROM THALES TO KEPLER.) This is the only work in English to give the complete history of man's cosmological views from prehistoric times to Kepler and Newton. Partial contents: Near Eastern astronomical systems, Early Greeks. Homocentric spheres of Eudoxus, Epicycles. Ptolemaic system, medieval cosmology. Copernicus. Kepler, etc. Revised, foreword by W. H. Stahl. New bibliography. xvii + 430pp. 5⅜ x 8. **S79 Paperbound $1.98**

THE PSYCHOLOGY OF INVENTION IN THE MATHEMATICAL FIELD, J. Hadamard. Where do ideas come from? What role does the unconscious play? Are ideas best developed by mathematical reasoning, word reasoning, visualization? What are the methods used by Einstein, Poincaré, Galton, Riemann. How can these techniques be applied by others? Hadamard, one of the world's leading mathematicians, discusses these and other questions. xiii + 145pp. 5⅜ x 8. **T107 Paperbound $1.25**

SPINNING TOPS AND GYROSCOPIC MOTION, John Perry. Well-known classic of science still unsurpassed for lucid, accurate, delightful exposition. How quasi-rigidity is induced in flexible and fluid bodies by rapid motion; why gyrostat falls, top rises; nature and effect on climatic conditions of earth's precessional movement; effect of internal fluidity on rotating bodies, etc. Appendixes describe practical uses to which gyroscopes have been put in ships, compasses, monorail transportation. 62 figures. 128pp. 5⅜ x 8. **T416 Paperbound $1.00**

A CONCISE HISTORY OF MATHEMATICS, D. Struik. Lucid study of development of mathematical ideas, techniques, from Ancient Near East, Greece, Islamic science, Middle Ages, Renaissance, modern times. Important mathematicians are described in detail. Treatment is not anecdotal, but analytical development of ideas. "Rich in content, thoughtful in interpretation" U. S. QUARTERLY BOOKLIST. Non-technical; no mathematical training needed. Index. 60 illustrations, including Egyptian papyri, Greek mss., portraits of 31 eminent mathematicians. Bibliography. 2nd edition. xix + 299pp. 5⅜ x 8.   S255 Paperbound **$1.75**

FOUNDATIONS OF GEOMETRY, Bertrand Russell. Analyzing basic problems in the overlap area between mathematics and philosophy, Nobel laureate Russell examines the nature of geometrical knowledge, the nature of geometry, and the application of geometry to space. It covers the history of non-Euclidean geometry, philosophic interpretations of geometry—especially Kant—projective and metrical geometry. This is most interesting as the solution offered in 1897 by a great mind to a problem still current. New introduction by Prof. Morris Kline of N. Y. University. xii + 201pp. 5⅜ x 8.   S232 Clothbound **$3.25**
                                                                                  S233 Paperbound **$1.60**

THE NATURE OF PHYSICAL THEORY, P. W. Bridgman. Here is how modern physics looks to a highly unorthodox physicist—a Nobel laureate. Pointing out many absurdities of science, and demonstrating the inadequacies of various physical theories, Dr. Bridgman weighs and analyzes the contributions of Einstein, Bohr, Newton, Heisenberg, and many others. This is a non-technical consideration of the correlation of science and reality. Index. xi + 138pp. 5⅜ x 8.
                                                                                  S33 Paperbound **$1.25**

EXPERIMENT AND THEORY IN PHYSICS, Max Born. A Nobel laureate examines the nature and value of the counterclaims of experiment and theory in physics. Synthetic versus analytical scientific advances are analyzed in the work of Einstein, Bohr, Heisenberg, Planck, Eddington, Milne, and others by a fellow participant. 44pp. 5⅜ x 8.   S308 Paperbound **60c**

THE STUDY OF THE HISTORY OF MATHEMATICS & THE STUDY OF THE HISTORY OF SCIENCE, George Sarton. Scientific method & philosophy in 2 scholarly fields. Defines duty of historian of math provides especially useful bibliography with best available biographies of modern mathematicians, editions of their collected works, correspondence. Shows that combination of history & science will aid scholar in understanding science today. Bibliography includes best known treatises on historical methods. 200-item critically evaluated bibliography. Index. 10 illustrations. 2 volumes bound as one. 113pp. + 75pp. 5⅜ x 8.   T240 Paperbound **$1.25**

SCIENCE AND METHOD, Henri Poincaré. Procedure of scientific discovery, methodology, experiment, idea-germination—the intellectual processes by which discoveries come into being. Most significant and most interesting aspects of development, application of ideas. Chapters cover selection of facts, chance, mathematical reasoning, mathematics and logic; Whitehead, Russell, Cantor; the new mechanics, etc. 288pp. 5⅜ x 8.   S222 Paperbound **$1.25**

SCIENCE AND HYPOTHESIS, Henri Poincaré. Creative psychology in science. How such concepts as number, magnitude, space, force, classical mechanics were developed, and how the modern scientist uses them in his thought. Hypothesis in physics, theories of modern physics. Introduction by Sir James Larmor. "Few mathematicians have had the breadth of vision of Poincaré, and none is his superior in the gift of clear exposition," E. T. Bell. Index. 272pp. 5⅜ x 8.
                                                                                  S221 Paperbound **$1.25**

FOUNDATIONS OF PHYSICS, R. B. Lindsay & H. Margenau. Excellent bridge between semi-popular works & technical treatises. A discussion of methods of physical description, construction of theory; valuable for physicist with elementary calculus who is interested in ideas that give meaning to data, tools of modern physics. Contents include symbolism, mathematical equations; space & time; foundations of mechanics; probability; physics & continua; electron theory; special & general relativity; quantum mechanics; causality. "Thorough and yet not overdetailed. Unreservedly recommended," NATURE (London). Unabridged, corrected edition. List of recommended readings. 35 illustrations. xi + 537pp. 5⅜ x 8.   S377 Paperbound **$2.45**

CLASSICS OF SCIENCE

THE THIRTEEN BOOKS OF EUCLID'S ELEMENTS, edited by **Sir Thomas Heath.** Definitive edition of one of the very greatest classics of Western world. Complete English translation of Heiberg text, together with spurious Book XIV. Detailed 150-page introduction discussing aspects of Greek and medieval mathematics. Euclid, texts, commentators, etc. Paralleling the text is an elaborate critical apparatus analyzing each definition, proposition, postulate, covering textual matters, mathematical analysis, commentators of all times, refutations, supports, extrapolations, etc. This is the full EUCLID. Unabridged reproduction of Cambridge U. 2nd edition. 3 volumes. Total of 995 figures, 1426pp. 5⅜ x 8.   S88,89,90 3 volume set, paperbound **$6.00**

OPTICKS, Sir Isaac Newton. In its discussions of light, reflection, color, refraction, theories of wave and corpuscular theories of light, this work is packed with scores of insights and discoveries. In its precise and practical discussion of construction of optical apparatus, contemporary understandings of phenomena it is truly fascinating to modern physicists, astronomers, mathematicians. Foreword by Albert Einstein. Preface by I. B. Cohen of Harvard University. 7 pages of portraits, facsimile pages, letters, etc. cxvi + 414pp. 5⅜ x 8.   S205 Paperbound **$2.00**

THE PRINCIPLE OF RELATIVITY, A. Einstein, H. Lorentz, M. Minkowski, H. Weyl. These are the 11 basic papers that founded the general and special theories of relativity, all translated into English. Two papers by Lorentz on the Michelson experiment, electromagnetic phenomena. Minkowski's SPACE & TIME, and Weyl's GRAVITATION & ELECTRICITY. 7 epoch-making papers by Einstein: ELECTROMAGNETICS OF MOVING BODIES, INFLUENCE OF GRAVITATION IN PROPAGATION OF LIGHT, COSMOLOGICAL CONSIDERATIONS, GENERAL THEORY, and 3 others. 7 diagrams. Special notes by A. Sommerfeld. 224pp. 5⅜ x 8.   S81 Paperbound **$1.75**

THE ANALYTICAL THEORY OF HEAT, Joseph Fourier. This book, which revolutionized mathematical physics, is listed in the Great Books program, and many other listings of great books. It has been used with profit by generations of mathematicians and physicists who are interested in either heat or in the application of the Fourier integral. Covers cause and reflections of rays of heat, radiant heating, heating of closed spaces, use of trigonometric series in the theory of heat, Fourier integral, etc. Translated by Alexander Freeman. 20 figures. xxii + 466pp. 5⅜ x 8.   S93 Paperbound **$2.00**

THE WORKS OF ARCHIMEDES, edited by T. L. Heath. All the known works of the great Greek mathematician are contained in this one volume, including the recently discovered Method of Archimedes. Contains: On Sphere & Cylinder, Measurement of a Circle, Spirals, Concids, Spheroids, etc. This is the definitive edition of the greatest mathematical intellect of the ancient world. 186-page study by Heath discusses Archimides and the history of Greek mathematics. Bibliography. 563pp. 5⅜ x 8.   S9 Paperbound **$2.00**

A PHILOSOPHICAL ESSAY ON PROBABILITIES, Marquis de Laplace. This famous essay explains without recourse to mathematics the principle of probability, and the application of probability to games of chance, natural philosophy, astronomy, many other fields. Translated from the 6th French edition by F. W. Truscott, F. L. Emory, with new introduction for this edition by E. T. Bell. 204pp. 5⅜ x 8.   S166 Paperbound **$1.25**

INVESTIGATIONS ON THE THEORY OF THE BROWNIAN MOVEMENT, Albert Einstein. Reprints from rare European journals. 5 basic papers, including the Elementary Theory of the Brownian Movement, written at the request of Lorentz to provide a simple explanation. Translated by A. D. Cowper. Annotated, edited by R. Fürth. 33pp. of notes elucidate, give history of previous investigations. Author, subject indexes. 62 footnotes. 124pp. 5⅜ x 8.
                                                                                S304 Paperbound **$1.25**

THE GEOMETRY OF RENÉ DESCARTES. With this book Descartes founded analytical geometry. Original French text, with Descartes' own diagrams, and excellent Smith-Latham translation. Contains Problems the Construction of Which Requires Only Straight Lines and Circles; On the Nature of Curved Lines; On the Construction of Solid or Supersolid Problems. Notes. Diagrams. 258pp. 5⅜ x 8.   S68 Paperbound **$1.50**

DIALOGUES CONCERNING TWO NEW SCIENCES, Galileo Galilei. This classic of experimental science, mechanics, engineering, is as enjoyable as it is important. Based on 30 years' experimentation and characterized by its author as ''superior to everything else of mine,'' it offers a lively exposition of dynamics, elasticity, sound, ballistics, strength of materials, and the scientific method. Translated by H. Grew and A. de Salvio. 126 diagrams. Index. xxi + 288pp. 5⅜ x 8.   S99 Paperbound **$1.65**

TREATISE ON ELECTRICITY AND MAGNETISM, James Clerk Maxwell. For more than 80 years a seemingly inexhaustible source of leads for physicists, mathematicians, engineers. Total of 1082pp. on such topics as Measurement of Quantities, Electrostatics, Elementary Mathematical Theory of Electricity, Electrical Work and Energy in a System of Conductors, General Theorems, Theory of Electrical Images, Electrolysis, Conduction, Polarization, Dielectrics, Resistance, etc. ''The greatest mathematical physicist since Newton,'' Sir James Jeans. 3rd edition. 107 figures, 21 plates. 1082pp. 5⅜ x 8.   S186 Clothbound **$4.95**

PRINCIPLES OF PHYSICAL OPTICS, Ernst Mach. This classical examination of the propagation of light, color, polarization etc. offers a historical and philosophical treatment that has never been surpassed for breadth and easy readability. Contents: Rectilinear propagation of light. Reflection, refraction. Early knowledge of vision. Dioptrics. Composition of light. Theory of color and dispersion. Periodicity. Theory of interference. Polarization. Mathematical representation of properties of light. Propagation of waves, etc. 279 illustrations, 10 portraits. Appendix. Indexes. 324pp. 5⅜ x 8.   S178 Paperbound **$1.75**

THEORY OF ELECTRONS AND ITS APPLICATION TO THE PHENOMENA OF LIGHT AND RADIANT HEAT, H. Lorentz. Lectures delivered at Columbia University by Nobel laureate Lorentz. Unabridged, they form a historical coverage of the theory of free electrons, motion, absorption of heat, Zeeman effect, propagation of light in molecular bodies, inverse Zeeman effect, optical phenomena in moving bodies, etc. 109 pages of notes explain the more advanced sections. Index. 9 figures. 352pp. 5⅜ x 8.   S173 Paperbound **$1.85**

MATTER & MOTION, James Clerk Maxwell. This excellent exposition begins with simple particles and proceeds gradually to physical systems beyond complete analysis: motion, force, properties of centre of mass of material system, work, energy, gravitation, etc. Written with all Maxwell's original insights and clarity! Notes by E. Larmor. 17 diagrams. 178pp. 5⅜ x 8.
                                                                                S188 Paperbound **$1.25**

AN INTRODUCTION TO THE STUDY OF EXPERIMENTAL MEDICINE, Claude Bernard. 90-year-old classic of medical science, only major work of Bernard available in English, records his efforts to transform physiology into exact science. Principles of scientific research illustrated by specific case histories from his work; roles of chance, error, preliminary false conclusions, in leading eventually to scientific truth; use of hypothesis. Much of modern application of mathematics to biology rests on the foundation set down here. New foreword by Professor I. B. Cohen, Harvard Univ. xxv + 266pp. 5⅜ x 8.   T400 Paperbound **$1.50**

PRINCIPLES OF MECHANICS, Heinrich Hertz. This last work by the great 19th century physicist is not only a classic, but of great interest in the logic of science. Creating a new system of mechanics based upon space, time, and mass, it returns to axiomatic analysis, to understanding of the formal or structural aspects of science, taking into account logic, observation, and a priori elements. Of great historical importance to Poincaré, Carnap, Einstein, Milne. A 20-page introduction by R. S. Cohen, Wesleyan University, analyzes the implications of Hertz's thought and the logic of science. Bibliography. 13-page introduction of Helmholtz. xiii + 274pp. 5⅜ x 8.
S316 Clothbound **$3.50**
S317 Paperbound **$1.75**

ANIMALS IN MOTION, Eadweard Muybridge. Largest, most comprehensive selection of Muybridge's famous action photos of animals, from his ANIMAL LOCOMOTION. 3919 high-speed shots of 34 different animals and birds in 123 different types of action: horses, mules, oxen, pigs, goats, camels, elephants, dogs, cats, guanacos, sloths, lions, tigers, jaguars, raccoons, baboons, deer, elk, gnus, kangaroos, many others, in different actions—walking, running, flying, leaping. Horse alone shown in more than 40 different ways. Photos taken against ruled backgrounds; most actions taken from 3 angles at once: 90°, 60°, rear. Most plates original size. Of considerable interest to scientists as a classic of biology, as a record of actual facts of natural history and physiology. "A really marvellous series of plates," NATURE (London). "A monumental work," Waldemar Kaempffert. Photographed by E. Muybridge. Edited by L. S. Brown, American Museum of Natural History. 74-page introduction on mechanics of motion. 340 pages of plates, 3919 photographs. 416pp. Deluxe binding, paper. (Weight 4½ lbs.) 7⅞ x 10⅝.
T203 Clothbound **$10.00**

THE HUMAN FIGURE IN MOTION, Eadweard Muybridge. This new edition of a great classic in the history of science and photography is the largest selection ever made from the original Muybridge photos of human action: 4789 photographs, illustrating 163 types of motion: walking, running, lifting, etc. in time-exposure sequence photos at speeds up to 1/6000th of a second. Men, women, children, mostly undraped, showing bone and muscle positions against ruled backgrounds, mostly taken at 3 angles at once. Not only was this a great work of photography, acclaimed by contemporary critics as a work of genius, it was also a great 19th century landmark in biological research. Historical introduction by Prof. Robert Taft, U. of Kansas. Plates original size, full detail. Over 500 action strips. 407pp. 7¾ x 10⅝.
T204 Clothbound **$10.00**

ON THE SENSATIONS OF TONE, Hermann Helmholtz. This is an unmatched coordination of such fields as acoustical physics, physiology, experiment, history of music. It covers the entire gamut of musical tone. Partial contents: relation of vibration, resonance, analysis of tones by sympathetic resonance, beats, chords, tonality, consonant chords, discords, progression of parts, etc. 33 appendixes discuss various aspects of sound, physics, acoustics, music, etc. Translated by A. J. Ellis. New introduction by Prof. Henry Margenau of Yale. 68 figures. 43 musical passages analyzed. Over 100 tables. Index. xix + 576pp. 6⅛ x 9¼.
S114 Clothbound **$4.95**

COLLECTED WORKS OF BERNHARD RIEMANN. This important source book is the first to contain the complete text of both 1892 Werke and the 1902 supplement, unabridged. It contains 31 monographs, 3 complete lecture courses, 15 miscellaneous papers, which have been of enormous importance in relativity, topology, theory of complex variables, and other areas of mathematics. Edited by R. Dedekind, H. Weber, M. Noether, W. Wirtinger. German text. English introduction by Hans Lewy. 690pp. 5⅜ x 8.
S226 Paperbound **$2.85**

CONTRIBUTIONS TO THE FOUNDING OF THE THEORY OF TRANSFINITE NUMBERS, Georg Cantor. These papers founded a new branch of mathematics. The famous articles of 1895-7 are translated with an 82-page introduction by P. E. B. Jourdain dealing with Cantor, the background of his discoveries, their results, future possibilities. Bibliography. Index. Notes. ix + 211pp. 5⅜ x 8.
S45 Paperbound **$1.25**

PRINCIPLES OF PSYCHOLOGY, William James. This is the complete "Long Course," which is not to be confused with abridged editions. It contains all the wonderful descriptions, deep insights that have caused it to be a permanent work in all psychological libraries. Partial contents: functions of the brain, automation theories, mind-stuff theories, relation of mind to other things, consciousness, times, space, thing perception, will, emotions, hypnotism, and dozens of other areas in descriptive psychology. "A permanent classic like Locke's ESSAYS, Hume's TREATISE," John Dewey. "The preeminence of James in American psychology is unquestioned," PERSONALIST. "The American classic in psychology—unequaled in breadth and scope in the entire psychological literature," PSYCHOANALYTICAL QUARTERLY. Index. 94 figures. 2 volumes bound as one. Total of 1408pp.
T381 Vol. 1. Paperbound **$2.00**
T382 Vol. 2. Paperbound **$2.00**

RECREATIONS

SEVEN SCIENCE FICTION NOVELS OF H. G. WELLS. This is the complete text, unabridged, of seven of Wells's greatest novels: War of the Worlds, The Invisible Man, The Island of Dr. Moreau, The Food of the Gods, The First Men in the Moon, In the Days of the Comet, The Time Machine. Still considered by many experts to be the best science-fiction ever written, they will offer amusement and instruction to the scientific-minded reader. 1015pp. 5⅜ x 8.
T264 Clothbound **$3.95**

28 SCIENCE FICTION STORIES OF H. G. WELLS. Unabridged! This enormous omnibus contains 2 full-length novels—Men Like Gods, Star Begotten—plus 26 short stories of space, time, invention, biology, etc. The Crystal Egg, The Country of the Blind, Empire of the Ants, The Man Who Could Work Miracles, Aepyornis Island, A Story of the Days to Come, and 22 others! 915pp. 5⅜ x 8.   T265 Clothbound **$3.95**

FLATLAND, E. A. Abbott. This is a perennially popular science-fiction classic about life in a two-dimensioned world, and the impingement of higher dimensions. Political, satiric, humorous, moral overtones. Relativity, the fourth dimension, and other aspects of modern science are explained more clearly than in most texts. 7th edition. New introduction by Banesh Hoffmann. 128pp. 5⅜ x 8.   T1 Paperbound **$1.00**

CRYPTANALYSIS, Helen F. Gaines. (Formerly ELEMENTARY CRYPTANALYSIS.) A standard elementary and intermediate text for serious students. It does not confine itself to old material, but contains much that is not generally known except to experts. Concealment, Transposition, Substitution ciphers; Vigenere, Kasiski, Playfair, multafid, dozens of other techniques. Appendix with sequence charts, letter frequencies in English, 5 other languages, English word frequencies. Bibliography. 167 codes. New to this edition: solutions to codes. vi + 230pp. 5⅜ x 8⅜.
                                                                        T97 Paperbound **$1.95**

FADS AND FALLACIES IN THE NAME OF SCIENCE, Martin Gardner. Examines various cults, quack systems, frauds, delusions which at various times have masqueraded as science. Accounts of hollow-earth fanatics like Symmes; Velikovsky and wandering planets; Hoerbiger; Bellamy and the theory of multiple moons; Charles Fort, dowsing, pseudoscientific methods for finding water, ores, oil. Sections on naturopathy, iridiagnosis, zone therapy, food fads, etc. Analytical accounts of Wilhelm Reich and orgone sex energy; L. Ron Hubbard and Dianetics; A. Korzybski and General Semantics; many others. Brought up to date to include Bridey Murphy, others. Not just a collection of anecdotes, but a fair, reasoned-appraisal of eccentric theory. Formerly titled IN THE NAME OF SCIENCE. Preface. Index. x + 384pp. 5⅜ x 8.
                                                                        T394 Paperbound **$1.50**

REINFELD ON THE END GAME IN CHESS, Fred Reinfeld. Analyzes 62 end games by Alekhine, Flohr, Tarrasch, Morphy, Bogolyubov, Capablanca, Vidmar, Rubinstein, Lasker, Reshevsky, other masters. Only first-rate book with extensive coverage of error; of immense aid in pointing out errors you might have made. Centers around transitions from middle play to various types of end play. King & pawn endings, minor piece endings, queen endings, bad bishops, blockage, weak pawns, passed pawns, etc. Formerly titled PRACTICAL END PLAY. 62 figures. vi + 177pp. 5⅜ x 8.   T417 Paperbound **$1.25**

PUZZLE QUIZ AND STUNT FUN, Jerome Meyer. 238 high-priority puzzles, stunts, and tricks—mathematical puzzles like The Clever Carpenter, Atom Bomb, Please Help Alice; mysteries and deductions like The Bridge of Sighs, Dog Logic, Secret Code; observation puzzlers like The American Flag, Playing Cards, Telephone Dial; more than 200 others involving magic squares, tongue twisters, puns, anagrams, word design. Answers included. Revised, enlarged edition of FUN-TO-DO. Over 100 illustrations. 238 puzzles, stunts, tricks. 256pp. 5⅜ x 8.
                                                                        T337 Paperbound **$1.00**

THE BOOK OF MODERN PUZZLES, G. L. Kaufman. More than 150 word puzzles, logic puzzles. No warmed-over fare but all new material based on same appeals that make crosswords and deduction puzzles popular, but with different principles, techniques. Two-minute teasers, involved word-labyrinths, design and pattern puzzles, puzzles calling for logic and observation, puzzles testing ability to apply general knowledge to peculiar situations, many others. Answers to all problems. 116 illustrations. 192pp. 5⅜ x 8.   T143 Paperbound **$1.00**

101 PUZZLES IN THOUGHT AND LOGIC by C. R. Wylie, Jr. Designed for readers who enjoy the challenge and stimulation of logical puzzles without specialized mathematical or scientific knowledge. These problems are entirely new and range from relatively easy, to brainteasers that will afford hours of subtle entertainment. Detective problems, how to find the lying fisherman, how a blindman can identify color by logic, and many more. Easy-to-understand introduction to the logic of puzzle solving and general scientific method. 128pp. 5⅜ x 8.
                                                                        T367 Paperbound **$1.00**

MATHEMAGIC, MAGIC PUZZLES, AND GAMES WITH NUMBERS, Royal V. Heath. Over 60 new puzzles and stunts based on properties of numbers. Demonstrates easy techniques for multiplying large numbers mentally, identifying unknown numbers, determining date of any day in any year, dozens of similar useful, entertaining applications of mathematics. Entertainments like The Lost Digit, 3 Acrobats, Psychic Bridge, magic squares, triangles, cubes, circles, other material not easily found elsewhere. Edited by J. S. Meyer. 76 illustrations. 128pp. 5⅜ x 8.
                                                                        T110 Paperpound **$1.00**

LEARN CHESS FROM THE MASTERS, Fred Reinfeld. Improve your chess, rate your improvement, by playing against Marshall, Znosko-Borovsky, Bronstein, Najdorf, others. Formerly titled CHESS BY YOURSELF, this book contains 10 games in which you move against masters, and grade your moves by an easy system. Games selected for interest, clarity, easy principles; illustrate common openings, both classical and modern. Ratings for 114 extra playing situations that might have arisen. Full annotations. 91 diagrams. viii + 144pp. 5¾ x 8.
                                                                        T362 Paperbound **$1.00**

THE COMPLETE NONSENSE OF EDWARD LEAR. Original text & illustrations of all Lear's nonsense books: A BOOK OF NONSENSE, NONSENSE SONGS, MORE NONSENSE SONGS, LAUGHABLE LYRICS, NONSENSE SONGS AND STORIES. Only complete edition available at popular price. Old favorites such as The Dong With a Luminous Nose, hundreds of other delightful bits of nonsense for children & adults. 214 different limericks, each illustrated by Lear; 3 different sets of Nonsense Botany; 5 Nonsense Alphabets; many others. 546 illustrations. 320pp. 5⅜ x 8.
T167 Paperbound **$1.00**

CRYPTOGRAPHY, D. Smith. Excellent elementary introduction to enciphering, deciphering secret writing. Explains transposition, substitution ciphers; codes; solutions. Geometrical patterns, route transcription, columnar transposition, other methods. Mixed cipher systems; single-alphabet, polyalphabetical substitution; mechanical devices; Vigenere system, etc. Enciphering Japanese; explanation of Baconian Biliteral cipher frequency tables. More than 150 problems provide practical application. Bibliography. Index. 164pp. 5⅜ x 8.
T247 Paperbound **$1.00**

MATHEMATICAL EXCURSIONS, Helen A. Merrill. Fun, recreation, insights into elementary problem-solving. A mathematical expert guides you along by-paths not generally travelled in elementary math courses—how to divide by inspection, Russian peasant system of multiplication; memory systems for pi; building odd and even magic squares; dyadic systems; facts about 37; square roots by geometry; Tchebichev's machine; drawing five-sided figures; dozens more. Solutions to more difficult ones. 50 illustrations. 145pp. 5⅜ x 8.
T350 Paperbound **$1.00**

MATHEMATICAL RECREATIONS, M. Kraitchik. Some 250 puzzles, problems, demonstrations of recreational mathematics for beginners & advanced mathematicians. Unusual historical problems from Greek, Medieval, Arabic, Hindu sources; modern problems based on "mathematics without numbers," geometry, topology, arithmetic, etc. Pastimes derived from figurative numbers, Mersenne numbers, Fermat numbers; fairy chess, latruncles, reversi, many other topics. Full solutions. Excellent for insights into special fields of math. 181 illustrations. 330pp. 5⅜ x 8.
T163 Paperbound **$1.75**

MATHEMATICAL PUZZLES FOR BEGINNERS AND ENTHUSIASTS, G. Mott-Smith. 188 mathematical puzzles to test mental agility. Inference, interpretation, algebra, dissection of plane figures, geometry, properties of numbers, decimation, permutations, probability, all enter these delightful problems. Puzzles like the Odic Force, How to Draw an Ellipse, Spider's Cousin, more than 180 others. Detailed solutions. Appendix with square roots, triangular numbers, primes, etc. 135 illustrations. 2nd revised edition. 248pp. 5⅜ x 8.
T198 Paperbound **$1.00**

NEW WORD PUZZLES, Gerald L. Kaufman. Contains 100 brand new challenging puzzles based on words and their combinations, never published before in any form. Most are new types invented by the author—for beginners or experts. Chess word puzzles, addle letter anagrams, double word squares, double horizontals, alphagram puzzles, dual acrostigrams, linkogram lapwords—plus 8 other brand new types, all with solutions included. 196 figures. 100 brand new puzzles. vi + 122pp. 5⅜ x 8.
T344 Paperbound **$1.00**

MATHEMATICS, MAGIC AND MYSTERY, Martin Gardner. Card tricks, feats of mental mathematics, stage mind-reading, other "magic" explained as applications of probability, sets, theory of numbers, topology, various branches of mathematics. Creative examination of laws and their application, with sources of new tricks and insights. 115 sections discuss tricks with cards, dice, coins; geometrical vanishing tricks, dozens of others. No sleight of hand needed; mathematics guarantees success. 115 illustrations. xii + 174pp. 5⅜ x 8.
T335 Paperbound **$1.00**

MATHEMATICS ELEMENTARY TO INTERMEDIATE

HOW TO CALCULATE QUICKLY, Henry Sticker. This handy volume offers a tried and true method for helping you in the basic mathematics of daily life—addition, subtraction, multiplication, division, fractions, etc. It is designed to awaken your "number sense" or the ability to see relationships between numbers as whole quantities. It is not a collection of tricks working only on special numbers, but a serious course of over 9,000 problems and their solutions, teaching special techniques not taught in schools: left-to-right multiplication, new fast ways of division, etc. 5 or 10 minutes daily use will double or triple your calculation speed. Excellent for the scientific worker who is at home in higher math, but is not satisfied with his speed and accuracy in lower mathematics. 256pp. 5 x 7¼.
T295 Paperbound **$1.00**

FAMOUS PROBLEMS OF ELEMENTARY GEOMETRY, Felix Klein. Expanded version of the 1894 Easter lectures at Göttingen. 3 problems of classical geometry: squaring circle, trisecting angle, doubling cube, considered with full modern implications: transcendental numbers, pi, etc. Notes by R. Archibald. 16 figures. xi + 92pp. 5⅜ x 8.
T348 Clothbound **$1.50**
T298 Paperbound **$1.00**

HIGHER MATHEMATICS FOR STUDENTS OF CHEMISTRY AND PHYSICS, J. W. Mellor. Not abstract, but practical, building its problems out of familiar laboratory material, this covers differential calculus, coordinate, analytical geometry, functions, integral calculus, infinite series, numerical equations, differential equations, Fourier's theorem, probability, theory of errors, calculus of variations, determinants. "If the reader is not familiar with this book, it will repay him to examine it," CHEM. & ENGINEERING NEWS. 800 problems, 189 figures. Bibliography. xxi + 641pp. 5⅜ x 8.
S193 Paperbound **$2.00**

TRIGONOMETRY REFRESHER FOR TECHNICAL MEN, A. Albert Klaf. 913 detailed questions and answers cover the most important aspects of plane and spherical trigonometry. They will help you to brush up or to clear up difficulties in special areas.—The first portion of this book covers plane trigonometry, including angles, quadrants, trigonometrical functions, graphical representation, interpolation, equations, logarithms, solution of triangle, use of the slide rule and similar topics—188 pages then discuss application of plane trigonometry to special problems in navigation, surveying, elasticity, architecture, and various fields of engineering. Small angles, periodic functions, vectors, polar coordinates, De Moivre's theorem are fully examined—The third section of the book then discusses spherical trigonometry and the solution of spherical triangles, with their applications to terrestrial and astronomical problems. Methods of saving time with numerical calculations, simplification of principal functions of angle, much practical information make this a most useful book—913 questions answered. 1738 problems, answers to odd numbers. 494 figures. 24 pages of useful formulae, functions. Index. x + 629pp. 5⅜ x 8.
T371 Paperbound **$2.00**

CALCULUS REFRESHER FOR TECHNICAL MEN, A. Albert Klaf. This book is unique in English as a refresher for engineers, technicians, students who either wish to brush up their calculus or to clear up uncertainties. It is not an ordinary text, but an examination of most important aspects of integral and differential calculus in terms of the 756 questions most likely to occur to the technical reader. The first part of this book covers simple differential calculus, with constants, variables, functions, increments, derivatives, differentiation, logarithms, curvature of curves, and similar topics—The second part covers fundamental ideas of integration, inspection, substitution, transformation, reduction, areas and volumes, mean value, successive and partial integration, double and triple integration. Practical aspects are stressed rather than theoretical. A 50-page section illustrates the application of calculus to specific problems of civil and nautical engineering, electricity, stress and strain, elasticity, industrial engineering, and similar fields.— 756 questions answered. 566 problems, mostly answered. 36 pages of useful constants, formulae for ready reference. Index. v + 431pp. 5⅜ x 8.
T370 Paperbound **$2.00**

MONOGRAPHS ON TOPICS OF MODERN MATHEMATICS, edited by J. W. A. Young. Advanced mathematics for persons who haven't gone beyond or have forgotten high school algebra. 9 monographs on foundation of geometry, modern pure geometry, non-Euclidean geometry, fundamental propositions of algebra, algebraic equations, functions, calculus, theory of numbers, etc. Each monograph gives proofs of important results, and descriptions of leading methods, to provide wide coverage. New introduction by Prof. M. Kline, N. Y. University. 100 diagrams. xvi + 416pp. 6⅛ x 9¼.
S289 Paperbound **$2.00**

MATHEMATICS: INTERMEDIATE TO ADVANCED

INTRODUCTION TO THE THEORY OF FOURIER'S SERIES AND INTEGRALS, H. S. Carslaw. 3rd revised edition. This excellent introduction is an outgrowth of the author's courses at Cambridge. Historical introduction, rational and irrational numbers, infinite sequences and series, functions of a single variable, definite integral, Fourier series, Fourier integrals, and similar topics. Appendixes discuss practical harmonic analysis, periodogram analysis, Lebesgues theory. Indexes. 84 examples, bibliography. xiii + 368 pp. 5⅜ x 8.
S48 Paperbound **$2.00**

INTRODUCTION TO THE THEORY OF NUMBERS, L. E. Dickson. Thorough, comprehensive approach with adequate coverage of classical literature, an introductory volume beginners can follow. Chapters on divisibility, congruences, quadratic residues & reciprocity, Diophantine equations, etc. Full treatment of binary quadratic forms without usual restriction to integral coefficients. Covers infinitude of primes, least residues, Fermat's theorem, Euler's phi function, Legendre's symbol, Gauss's lemma, automorphs, reduced forms, recent theorems of Thue & Siegel, many more. Much material not readily available elsewhere. 239 problems. Index. 1 figure. viii + 183pp. 5⅜ x 8.
S342 Paperbound **$1.65**

MECHANICS VIA THE CALCULUS, P. W. Norris, W. S. Legge. Covers almost everything from linear motion to vector analysis: equations determining motion, linear methods, compounding of simple harmonic motions, Newton's laws of motion, Hooke's law, the simple pendulum, motion of a particle in 1 plane, centers of gravity, virtual work, friction, kinetic energy of rotating bodies, equilibrium of strings, hydrostatics, sheering stresses, elasticity, etc. 550 problems. 3rd revised edition. xii + 367pp.
S207 Clothbound **$3.95**

NON-EUCLIDEAN GEOMETRY, Roberto Bonola. The standard coverage of non-Euclidean geometry. It examines from both a historical and mathematical point of view the geometries which have arisen from a study of Euclid's 5th postulate upon parallel lines. Also included are complete texts, translated, of Bolyai's THEORY OF ABSOLUTE SPACE, Lobachevsky's THEORY OF PARALLELS. 180 diagrams. 431pp. 5⅜ x 8.
S27 Paperbound **$1.95**

ELEMENTS OF THE THEORY OF REAL FUNCTIONS, J. E. Littlewood. Based on lectures given at Trinity College, Cambridge, this book has proved to be extremely successful in introducing graduate students to the modern theory of functions. It offers a full and concise coverage of classes and cardinal numbers, well-ordered series, other types of series, and elements of the theory of sets of points. 3rd revised edition. vii + 71pp. 5⅜ x 8.
S171 Clothbound **$2.85**
S172 Paperbound **$1.25**

THE CONTINUUM AND OTHER TYPES OF SERIAL ORDER, E. V. Huntington. This famous book gives a systematic elementary account of the modern history of the continuum as a type of serial order. Based on the Cantor-Dedekind ordinal theory, which requires no technical knowledge of higher mathematics, it offers an easily followed analysis of ordered classes, discrete and dense series, continuous series, Cantor's transfinite numbers. 2nd edition. Index. viii + 82pp. 5⅜ x 8.
S129 Clothbound **$2.75**
S130 Paperbound **$1.00**

GEOMETRY OF FOUR DIMENSIONS, H. P. Manning. Unique in English as a clear, concise introduction. Treatment is synthetic, and mostly Euclidean, although in hyperplanes and hyperspheres at infinity, non-Euclidean geometry is used. Historical introduction. Foundations of 4-dimensional geometry. Perpendicularity, simple angles. Angles of planes, higher order. Symmetry, order, motion; hyperpyramids, hypercones, hyperspheres; figures with parallel elements; volume, hypervolume in space; regular polyhedroids. Glossary. 78 figures. ix + 348pp. 5⅜ x 8.
S181 Clothbound **$3.95**
S182 Paperbound **$1.95**

VECTOR AND TENSOR ANALYSIS, G. E. Hay. One of the clearest introductions to this increasingly important subject. Start with simple definitions, finish the book with a sure mastery of oriented Cartesian vectors, Christoffel symbols, solenoidal tensors, and their applications. Complete breakdown of plane, solid, analytical, differential geometry. Separate chapters on application. All fundamental formulae listed & demonstrated. 195 problems, 66 figures. viii + 193pp. 5⅜ x 8.
S109 Paperbound **$1.75**

INTRODUCTION TO THE DIFFERENTIAL EQUATIONS OF PHYSICS, L. Hopf. Especially valuable to the engineer with no math beyond elementary calculus. Emphasizing intuitive rather than formal aspects of concepts, the author covers an extensive territory. Partial contents: Law of causality, energy theorem, damped oscillations, coupling by friction, cylindrical and spherical coordinates, heat source, etc. Index. 48 figures. 160pp. 5⅜ x 8. S120 Paperbound **$1.25**

INTRODUCTION TO THE THEORY OF GROUPS OF FINITE ORDER, R. Carmichael. Examines fundamental theorems and their application. Beginning with sets, systems, permutations, etc., it progresses in easy stages through important types of groups: Abelian, prime power, permutation, etc. Except 1 chapter where matrices are desirable, no higher math needed. 783 exercises, problems. Index. xvi + 447pp. 5⅜ x 8.
S299 Clothbound **$3.95**
S300 Paperbound **$2.00**

THEORY OF GROUPS OF FINITE ORDER, W. Burnside. First published some 40 years ago, this is still one of the clearest introductory texts. Partial contents: permutations, groups independent of representation, composition series of a group, isomorphism of a group with itself, Abelian groups, prime power groups, permutation groups, invariants of groups of linear substitution, graphical representation, etc. 45pp. of notes. Indexes. xxiv + 512pp. 5⅜ x 8.
S38 Paperbound **$2.45**

INFINITE SEQUENCES AND SERIES, Konrad Knopp. First publication in any language! Excellent introduction to 2 topics of modern mathematics, designed to give the student background to penetrate farther by himself. Sequences & sets, real & complex numbers, etc. Functions of a real & complex variable. Sequences & series. Infinite series. Convergent power series. Expansion of elementary functions. Numerical evaluation of series. Bibliography. v + 186pp. 5⅜ x 8.
S152 Clothbound **$3.50**
S153 Paperbound **$1.75**

THEORY OF SETS, E. Kamke. Clearest, amplest introduction in English, well suited for independent study. Subdivisions of main theory, such as theory of sets of points, are discussed, but emphasis is on general theory. Partial contents: rudiments of set theory, arbitrary sets and their cardinal numbers, ordered sets and their order types, well-ordered sets and their ordinal numbers. Bibliography. Key to symbols. Index. vii + 144pp. 5⅜ x 8. S141 Paperbound **$1.35**

ELEMENTS OF NUMBER THEORY, I. M. Vinogradov. Detailed 1st course for persons without advanced mathematics; 95% of this book can be understood by readers who have gone no farther than high school algebra. Partial contents: divisibility theory, important number theoretical functions, congruences, primitive roots and indices, etc. Solutions to both problems and exercises. Tables of primes, indices, etc. Covers almost every essential formula in elementary number theory! 233 problems, 104 exercises. viii + 227pp. 5⅜ x 8. S259 Paperbound **$1.60**

FIVE VOLUME "THEORY OF FUNCTIONS" SET BY KONRAD KNOPP. This five-volume set, prepared by Konrad Knopp, provides a complete and readily followed account of theory of functions. Proofs are given concisely, yet without sacrifice of completeness or rigor. These volumes are used as texts by such universities as M.I.T., University of Chicago, N. Y. City College, and many others. "Excellent introduction . . . remarkably readable, concise, clear, rigorous," JOURNAL OF THE AMERICAN STATISTICAL ASSOCIATION.

ELEMENTS OF THE THEORY OF FUNCTIONS, Konrad Knopp. This book provides the student with background for further volumes in this set, or texts on a similar level. Partial contents: Foundations, system of complex numbers and the Gaussian plane of numbers, Riemann sphere of numbers, mapping by linear functions, normal forms, the logarithm, the cyclometric functions and binomial series. "Not only for the young student, but also for the student who knows all about what is in it," MATHEMATICAL JOURNAL. Bibliography. Index. 140pp. 5⅜ x 8. S154 Paperbound **$1.35**

THEORY OF FUNCTIONS, PART I., Konrad Knopp. With volume II, this book provides coverage of basic concepts and theorems. Partial contents: numbers and points, functions of a complex variable, integral of a continuous function, Cauchy's integral theorem, Cauchy's integral formulae, series with variable terms, expansion of analytic functions in power series, analytic continuation and complete definition of analytic functions, entire transcendental functions, Laurent expansion, types of singularities. Bibliography. Index. vii + 146pp. 5⅜ x 8.   S156 Paperbound **$1.35**

THEORY OF FUNCTIONS, PART II., Konrad Knopp. Application and further development of general theory, special topics. Single valued functions: entire, Weierstrass. Meromorphic functions: Mittag-Leffler. Periodic functions. Multiple-valued functions. Riemann surfaces. Algebraic functions. Analytical configuration, Riemann surface. Bibliography. Index. x + 150pp. 5⅜ x 8.
S157 Paperbound **$1.35**

PROBLEM BOOK IN THE THEORY OF FUNCTIONS, VOLUME 1., Konrad Knopp. Problems in elementary theory, for use with Knopp's THEORY OF FUNCTIONS, or any other text, arranged according to increasing difficulty. Fundamental concepts, sequences of numbers and infinite series, complex variable, integral theorems, development in series, conformal mapping. Answers. viii + 126pp. 5⅜ x 8.   S158 Paperbound **$1.35**

PROBLEM BOOK IN THE THEORY OF FUNCTIONS, VOLUME 2, Konrad Knopp. Advanced theory of functions, to be used either with Knopp's THEORY OF FUNCTIONS, or any other comparable text. Singularities, entire & meromorphic functions, periodic, analytic, continuation, multiple-valued functions, Riemann surfaces, conformal mapping. Includes a section of additional elementary problems. "The difficult task of selecting from the immense material of the modern theory of functions the problems just within the reach of the beginner is here masterfully accomplished," AM. MATH. SOC. Answers. 138pp. 5⅜ x 8.   S159 Paperbound **$1.35**

SYMBOLIC LOGIC

AN INTRODUCTION TO SYMBOLIC LOGIC, Susanne K. Langer. Probably the clearest book ever written on symbolic logic for the philosopher, general scientist and layman. It will be particularly appreciated by those who have been rebuffed by other introductory works because of insufficient mathematical training. No special knowledge of mathematics is required. Starting with the simplest symbols and conventions, you are led to a remarkable grasp of the Boole-Schroeder and Russell-Whitehead systems clearly and quickly. PARTIAL CONTENTS: Study of forms, Essentials of logical structure, Generalization, Classes, The deductive system of classes, The algebra of logic, Abstraction of interpretation, Calculus of propositions, Assumptions of PRINCIPIA MATHEMATICA, Logistics, Logic of the syllogism, Proofs of theorems. "One of the clearest and simplest introductions to a subject which is very much alive. The style is easy, symbolism is introduced gradually, and the intelligent non-mathematican should have no difficulty in following argument," MATHEMATICS GAZETTE. Revised, expanded second edition. Truth-value tables. 368pp. 5⅜ x 8.
S164 Paperbound **$1.75**

THE ELEMENTS OF MATHEMATICAL LOGIC, Paul Rosenbloom. FIRST PUBLICATION IN ANY LANGUAGE. This book is intended for readers who are mature mathematically, but have no previous training in symbolic logic. It does not limit itself to a single system, but covers the field as a whole. It is a development of lectures given at Lund University, Sweden in 1948. Partial contents: Logic of classes, fundamental theorems, Boolean algebra, logic of propositions, logic of propositional functions, expressive languages, combinatory logics, development of mathematics within an object language, paradoxes, theorems of Post and Goedel, Church's theorem, and similar topics. iv + 214pp. 5⅜ x 8.   S277 Paperbound **$1.45**

THE LAWS OF THOUGHT, George Boole. This book founded symbolic logic some hundred years ago. It is the 1st significant attempt to apply logic to all aspects of human endeavour. Partial contents: derivation of laws, signs & laws, interpretations, eliminations, conditions of a perfect method, analysis, Aristotelian logic, probability, and similar topics. xviii + 424pp. 5⅜ x 8.
S28 Paperbound **$2.00**

ELEMENTARY MATHEMATICS FROM AN
ADVANCED STANDPOINT, Felix Klein.

This classic text is an outgrowth of Klein's famous integration and survey course at Göttingen. Using one field of mathematics to interpret, adjust, illuminate another, it covers basic topics in each area, illustrating its discussion with extensive analysis. It is especially valuable in considering areas of modern mathematics. "Makes the reader feel the inspiration of . . . a great mathematician, inspiring teacher . . . with deep insight into the foundations and interrelations," BULLETIN, AMERICAN MATHEMATICAL SOCIETY.

Vol. 1. ARITHMETIC, ALGEBRA, ANALYSIS. Introducing the concept of function immediately, it enlivens abstract discussion with graphical and geometrically perceptual methods. Partial contents: natural numbers, extension of the notion of number, special properties, complex numbers. Real equations with real unknowns, complex quantities. Logarithmic, exponential functions, goniometric functions, infinitesimal calculus. Transcendence of e and pi, theory of assemblages. Index. 125 figures. ix + 247pp. 5⅜ x 8.   S150, Paperbound **$1.75**

Vol. 2. GEOMETRY. A comprehensive view which accompanies the space perception inherent in geometry with analytic formulas which facilitate precise formulation. Partial contents: Simplest geometric manifolds: line segment, Grassmann determinant principles, classification of configurations of space, derivative manifolds. Geometric transformations: affine transformations, projective, higher point transformations, theory of the imaginary. Systematic discussion of geometry and its foundations. Indexes. 141 illustrations. ix + 214pp. 5⅜ x 8.   S151 Paperbound **$1.75**

MATHEMATICS: ADVANCED

ALMOST PERIODIC FUNCTIONS, A. S. Besicovitch. This unique and important summary by a well-known mathematician covers in detail the two stages of development in Bohr's theory of almost periodic functions: (1) as a generalization of pure periodicity, with results and proofs; (2) the work done by Stepanoff, Wiener, Weyl, and Bohr in generalizing the theory. Bibliography. xi + 180pp. 5⅜ x 8.
S17 Clothbound **$3.50**
S18 Paperbound **$1.75**

LECTURES ON THE ICOSAHEDRON AND THE SOLUTION OF EQUATIONS OF THE FIFTH DEGREE, Felix Klein. The solution of quintics in terms of rotations of a regular icosahedron around its axes of symmetry. A classic & indispensable source for those interested in higher algebra, geometry, crystallography. Considerable explanatory material included. 230 footnotes, mostly bibliographic. 2nd edition, xvi + 289pp. 5⅜ x 8.
S314 Paperbound **$1.85**

LINEAR INTEGRAL EQUATIONS, W. V. Lovitt. Systematic survey of general theory, with some application to differential equations, calculus of variations problems of math, physics. Partial contents: integral equations of 2nd kind by successive substitutions; Fredholm's equation as ratio of 2 integral series in lambda, applications of the Fredholm theory, Hilbert-Schmidt theory of symmetric kernels, application, etc. Neumann, Dirichlet, vibratory problems. Index. ix + 253pp. 5⅜ x 8.
S175 Clothbound **$3.50**
S176 Paperbound **$1.60**

MATHEMATICAL FOUNDATIONS OF STATISTICAL MECHANICS, A. I. Khinchin. Offering a precise and rigorous formulation of problems, this book supplies a thorough and up-to-date exposition. It provides analytical tools needed to replace cumbersome concepts, and furnishes for the first time a logical step-by-step introduction to the subject. Partial contents: geometry & kinematics of the phase space, ergodic problem, reduction to theory of probability, application of central limit problem, ideal monatomic gas, foundation of thermodynamics, dispersion and distributions of sum functions. Key to notations. Index. xiii + 179p| . 5⅜ x 8.
S146 Clothbound **$2.95**
S147 Paperbound **$1.35**

ORDINARY DIFFERENTIAL EQUATIONS, E. L. Ince. A most compendious analysis in real and complex domains. Existence and nature of solutions, continuous transformation groups, solutions in an infinite form, definite integrals, algebraic theory, Sturmian theory, boundary problems, existence theorems, 1st order, higher order, etc. "Deserves the highest praise, a notable addition to mathematical literature," BULLETIN, AM. MATH. SOC. Historical appendix. Bibliography. 18 figures. viii + '558pp. 5⅜ x 8.
S349 Paperbound **$2.55**

TRIGONOMETRICAL SERIES, Antoni Zygmund. Unique in any language on modern advanced level. Contains carefully organized analyses of trigonometric, orthogonal, Fourier systems of functions, with clear adequate descriptions of summability of Fourier series, proximation theory, conjugate series, convergence, divergence of Fourier series. Especially valuable for Russian, Eastern European coverage. Bibliography. 329pp. 5⅜ x 8.
S290 Paperbound **$1.50**

FOUNDATIONS OF POTENTIAL THEORY, O. D. Kellogg. Based on courses given at Harvard this is suitable for both advanced and beginning mathematicians. Proofs are rigorous, and much material not generally available elsewhere is included. Partial contents: forces of gravity, fields of force, divergence theorem, properties of Newtonian potentials at points of free space, potentials as solutions of Laplace's equations, harmonic functions, electrostatics, electric images, logarithmic potential, etc. ix + 384pp. 5⅜ x 8.
S144 Paperbound **$1.98**

LECTURES ON CAUCHY'S PROBLEMS, J. Hadamard. Based on lectures given at Columbia and Rome, this discusses work of Riemann, Kirchhoff, Volterra, and the author's own research on the hyperbolic case in linear partial differential equations. It extends spherical and cylindrical waves to apply to all (normal) hyperbolic equations. Partial contents: Cauchy's problem, fundamental formula, equations with odd number, with even number of independent variables; method of descent. 32 figures. Index. iii + 361pp. 5⅜ x 8.
S105 Paperbound **$1.75**

MATHEMATICAL PHYSICS, STATISTICS

THE MATHEMATICAL THEORY OF ELASTICITY, A. E. H. Love. A wealth of practical illustration combined with thorough discussion of fundamentals—theory, application, special problems and solutions. Partial contents: Analysis of Strain & Stress, Elasticity of Solid Bodies, Isotropic Elastic Solids, Equilibrium of Aeolotropic Elastic Solids, Elasticity of Crystals, Vibration of Spheres, Cylinders, Propagation of Waves in Elastic Solid Media, Torsion, Theory of Continuous Beams, Plates. Rigorous treatment of Volterra's theory of dislocations, 2-dimensional elastic systems, other topics of modern interest. "For years the standard treatise on elasticity," AMERICAN MATHEMATICAL MONTHLY. 4th revised edition. Index. 76 figures. xviii + 643pp. 6⅛ x 9¼.
S174 Paperbound **$2.95**

TABLES OF FUNCTIONS WITH FORMULAE AND CURVES, E. Jahnke & F. Emde. The world's most comprehensive 1-volume English-text collection of tables, formulae, curves of transcendent functions. 4th corrected edition, new 76-page section giving tables, formulae for elementary functions—not in other English editions. Partial contents: sine, cosine, logarithmic integral; factorial function; error integral; theta functions; elliptic integrals, functions; Legendre, Bessel, Riemann, Mathieu, hypergeometric functions, etc. Supplementary books. Bibliography. Indexed. "Out of the way functions for which we know no other source," SCIENTIFIC COMPUTING SERVICE, Ltd. 212 figures. 400pp. 5⅜ x 8.
S133 Paperbound **$2.00**

PRACTICAL ANALYSIS, GRAPHICAL AND NUMERICAL METHODS, F. A. Willers. Translated by R. T. Beyer. Immensely practical handbook for engineers, showing how to interpolate, use various methods of numerical differentiation and integration, determine the roots of a single algebraic equation, system of linear equations, use empirical formulas, integrate differential equations, etc. Hundreds of shortcuts for arriving at numerical solutions. Special section on American calculating machines, by T. W. Simpson. 132 illustrations. 422pp. $5\frac{3}{8} \times 8$.   S273 Paperbound **$2.00**

DICTIONARY OF CONFORMAL REPRESENTATIONS, H. Kober. Laplace's equation in 2 dimensions solved in this unique book developed by the British Admiralty. Scores of geometrical forms & their transformations for electrical engineers, Joukowski aerofoil for aerodynamists, Schwartz-Christoffel transformations for hydrodynamics, transcendental functions. Contents classified according to analytical functions describing transformation. Twin diagrams show curves of most transformations with corresponding regions. Glossary. Topological index. 447 diagrams. 244pp. $6\frac{1}{8} \times 9\frac{1}{4}$.   S160 Paperbound **$2.00**

FREQUENCY CURVES AND CORRELATION, W. P. Elderton. 4th revised edition of a standard work covering classical statistics. It is practical in approach, and one of the books most frequently referred to for clear presentation of basic material. Partial contents. Frequency distributions. Method of moment. Pearson's frequency curves. Correlation. Theoretical distributions, spurious correlation. Correlation of characters not quantitatively measurable. Standard errors. Test of goodness of fit. The correlation ratio—contingency. Partial correlation. Corrections for moments, beta and gamma functions, etc. Key to terms, symbols. Bibliography. 25 examples in text. 40 useful tables. 16 figures. xi + 272pp. $5\frac{1}{2} \times 8\frac{1}{2}$.   Clothbound **$1.49**

HYDRODYNAMICS, H. Dryden, F. Murnaghan, Harry Bateman. Published by the National Research Council in 1932 this enormous volume offers a complete coverage of classical hydrodynamics. Encyclopedic in quality. Partial contents: physics of fluids, motion, turbulent flow, compressible fluids, motion in 1, 2, 3 dimensions; viscous fluids rotating, laminar motion, resistance of motion through viscous fluid, eddy viscosity, hydraulic flow in channels of various shapes, discharge of gases, flow past obstacles, etc. Bibliography of over 2,900 items. Indexes. 23 figures. 634pp. $5\frac{3}{8} \times 8$.   S303 Paperbound **$2.75**

HYDRODYNAMICS, A STUDY OF LOGIC, FACT, AND SIMILITUDE, Garrett Birkhoff. A stimulating application of pure mathematics to an applied problem. Emphasis is placed upon correlation of theory and deduction with experiment. It examines carefully recently discovered paradoxes, the ory of modelling and dimensional analysis, paradox & error in flows and free boundary theory. The author derives the classical theory of virtual mass from homogeneous spaces, and applies group theory to fluid mechanics. Index. Bibliography. 20 figures, 3 plates. xiii + 186pp. $5\frac{3}{8} \times 8$.
S21 Clothbound **$3.50**
S22 Paperbound **$1.85**

HYDRODYNAMICS, Horace Lamb. Internationally famous complete coverage of standard reference work on dynamics of liquids & gases. Fundamental theorems, equations, methods, solutions, background, for classical hydrodynamics. Chapters include Equations of Motion, Integration of Equations in Special Gases, Irrotational Motion, Motion of Liquid in 2 Dimensions, Motion of Solids through Liquid—Dynamical Theory, Vortex Motion, Tidal Waves, Surface Waves, Waves of Expansion, Viscosity, Rotating Masses of Liquids. Excellently planned, arranged; clear, lucid presentation. 6th enlarged, revised edition. Index. Over 900 footnotes, mostly bibliographical. 119 figures. xv + 738pp. $6\frac{1}{8} \times 9\frac{1}{4}$.   S256 Paperbound **$2.95**

INTRODUCTION TO RELAXATION METHODS, F. S. Shaw. Fluid mechanics, design of electrical networks, forces in structural frameworks, stress distribution, buckling, etc. Solve linear simultaneous equations, linear ordinary differential equations, partial differential equations, Eigenvalue problems by relaxation methods. Detailed examples throughout. Special tables for dealing with awkwardly-shaped boundaries. Indexes. 253 diagrams. 72 tables. 400pp. $5\frac{3}{8} \times 8$.
S244 Paperbound **$2.45**

PARTIAL DIFFERENTIAL EQUATIONS OF MATHEMATICAL PHYSICS, A. G. Webster. A keystone work in the library of every mature physicist, engineer, researcher. Valuable sections on elasticity, compression theory, potential theory, theory of sound, heat conduction, wave propagation, vibration theory. Contents include: deduction of differential equations, vibrations, normal functions, Fourier's series, Cauchy's method, boundary problems, method of Riemann-Volterra. Spherical, cylindrical, ellipsoidal harmonics, applications, etc. 97 figures. vii + 440pp. $5\frac{3}{8} \times 8$.
S263 Paperbound **$1.98**

THE THEORY OF GROUPS AND QUANTUM MECHANICS, H. Weyl. Discussions of Schroedinger's wave equation, de Broglie's waves of a particle, Jordon-Hoelder theorem, Lie's continuous groups of transformations, Pauli exclusion principle, quantization of Maxwell-Dirac field equations, etc. symmetry permutation group, algebra of symmetric transformation, etc. 2nd revised edition. Unitary geometry, quantum theory, groups, application of groups to quantum mechanics, symmetry permutation group, algebra of symmetric transformation, etc. 2nd revised edition. Bibliography. Index. xxii + 422pp. $5\frac{3}{8} \times 8$.   S268 Clothbound **$4.50**
S269 Paperbound **$1.95**

PARTIAL DIFFERENTIAL EQUATIONS OF MATHEMATICAL PHYSICS, Harry Bateman. Solution of boundary value problems by means of definite analytical expressions, with wide range of representative problems, full reference to contemporary literature, and new material by the author. Partial contents: classical equations, integral theorems of Green, Stokes; 2-dimensional problems; conformal representation; equations in 3 variables; polar coordinates; cylindrical, ellipsoidal, paraboloid, toroidal coordinates; non-linear equations, etc. "Must be in the hands of everyone interested in boundary value problems," BULLETIN, AM. MATH. SOC. Indexes. 450 bibliographic footnotes. 175 examples. 29 illustrations. xxii + 552pp. 6×9.   S15 Clothbound **$4.95**

NUMERICAL SOLUTIONS OF DIFFERENTIAL EQUATIONS, H. Levy & E. A. Baggott. Comprehensive collection of methods for solving ordinary differential equations of first and higher order. All must pass 2 requirements: easy to grasp and practical, more rapid than school methods. Partial contents: graphical integration of differential equations, graphical methods for detailed solution. Numerical solution. Simultaneous equations and equations of 2nd and higher orders. "Should be in the hands of all in research in applied mathematics, teaching," NATURE. 21 figures. viii + 238pp. 5⅜ x 8.   S168 Paperbound **$1.75**

ASYMPTOTIC EXPANSIONS, A. Erdélyi. The only modern work available in English, this is an unabridged reproduction of a monograph prepared for the Office of Naval Research. It discusses various procedures for asymptotic evaluation of integrals containing a large parameter and solutions of ordinary linear differential equations. Bibliography of 71 items. vi + 108pp. 5⅜ x 8.
S318 Paperbound **$1.35**

THE FOURIER INTEGRAL AND CERTAIN OF ITS APPLICATIONS, Norbert Wiener. The only book-length study of the Fourier integral as link between pure and applied math. An expansion of lectures given at Cambridge. Partial contents: Plancherel's theorem, general Tauberian theorem, special Tauberian theorms, generalized harmonic analysis. Bibliography. viii + 201pp. 5⅜ x 8.
S272 Clothbound **$3.95**

THE THEORY OF SOUND, Lord Rayleigh. Most vibrating systems likely to be encountered in practice can be tackled successfully by the methods set forth by the great Noble laureate, Lord Rayleigh. Complete coverage of experimental, mathematical aspects of sound theory. Partial contents: Harmonic motions, vibrating systems in general, lateral vibrations of bars, curved plates or shells, applications of Laplace's functions to acoustical problems, fluid friction, plane vortex-sheet, vibrations of solid bodies, etc. This is the first inexpensive edition of this great reference and study work. Bibliography. Historical introduction by R. B. Lindsay. Total of 1040pp. 97 figures. 5⅜ x 8.   S292, S293, Two volume set, paperbound **$4.00**

ANALYSIS & DESIGN OF EXPERIMENTS, H. B. Mann. Offers a method for grasping the analysis of variance and variance design within a short time. Partial contents: Chi-square distribution and analysis of variance distribution, matrices, quadratic forms, likelihood ratio tests and tests of linear hypotheses, power of analysis, Galois fields, non-orthogonal data, interblock estimates, etc. 15pp. of useful tables. x + 195pp. 5 x 7⅜.   S180 Paperbound **$1.45**

MATHEMATICAL ANALYSIS OF ELECTRICAL AND OPTICAL WAVE-MOTION, Harry Bateman. Written by one of this century's most distinguished mathematical physicists, this is a practical introduction to those developments of Maxwell's electromagnetic theory which are directly connected with the solution of the partial differential equation of wave motion. Methods of solving wave-equations, polar-cylindrical coordinates, diffraction, transformation of coordinates, homogeneous solutions, electromagnetic fields with moving singularities, etc. Index. 168pp. 5⅜ x 8.
S14 Paperbound **$1.60**

PHYSICAL PRINCIPLES OF THE QUANTUM THEORY, Werner Heisenberg. A Nobel laureate discusses quantum theory; Heisenberg's own work, Compton, Schroedinger, Wilson, Einstein, many others. Written for physicists, chemists who are not specialists in quantum theory, only elementary formulae are considered in the text; there is a mathematical appendix for specialists. Profound without sacrifice of clarity. Translated by C. Eckart, F. Hoyt. 18 figures. 192pp. 5⅜ x 8.
S113 Paperbound **$1.25**

FOUNDATIONS OF NUCLEAR PHYSICS, edited by R. T. Beyer. 13 of the most important papers on nuclear physics reproduced in facsimile in the original languages of their authors: the papers most often cited in footnotes, bibliographies. Anderson, Curie, Joliot, Chadwick, Fermi, Lawrence, Cockcroft, Hahn, Yukawa. Unparalleled Bibliography: 122 double-columned pages, over 4,000 articles, books, classified. 57 figures. 288pp. 6⅛ x 9¼.   S19 Paperbound **$1.75**

SELECTED PAPERS ON NOISE AND STOCHASTIC PROCESS, edited by Prof. Nelson Wax, U. of Illinois. 6 basic papers for newcomers in the field, for those whose work involves noise characteristics. Chandrasekhar, Uhlenbeck & Ornstein, Uhlenbeck & Ming, Rice, Doob. Included is Kac's Chauvenet-Prize winning Random Walk. Extensive bibliography lists 200 articles; up through 1953. 21 figures. 337pp. 6⅛ x 9¼.   S262 Paperbound **$2.25**

THERMODYNAMICS, Enrico Fermi. Unabridged reproduction of 1937 edition. Elementary in treatment; remarkable for clarity, organization. Requires no knowledge of advanced math beyond calculus, only familiarity with fundamentals of thermometry, calorimetry. Partial Contents: Thermodynamic systems; First & Second laws of thermodynamics; Entropy; Thermodynamic potentials: phase rule, reversible electric cell; Gaseous reactions: Van't Hoff reaction box, principle of LeChatelier; Thermodynamics of dilute solutions:: osmotic & vapor pressure, boiling & freezing points; Entropy constant. Index. 25 problems. 24 illustrations. x + 160pp. 5⅜ x 8.
S361 Paperbound **$1.75**

AN INTRODUCTION TO THE STUDY OF STELLAR STRUCTURE, Subrahmanyan Chandrasekhar. Outstanding treatise on stellar dynamics by one of world's greatest astrophysicists. Uses classical & modern math methods to examine relationship between loss of energy, the mass, and radius of stars in a steady state. Discusses thermodynamic laws from Caratheodory's axiomatic standpoint; adiabatic, polytropic laws; work of Ritter, Emden, Kelvin, others; Stroemgren envelopes as starter for theory of gaseous stars; Gibbs statistical mechanics (quantum); degenerate stellar configurations & theory of white dwarfs, etc. "Highest level of scientific merit," BULLETIN, AMER. MATH. SOC. Bibliography. Appendixes. Index. 33 figures. 509pp. 5⅜ x 8.
S413 Paperbound **$2.75**

APPLIED OPTICS AND OPTICAL DESIGN, A. E. Conrady. Thorough, systematic presentation of physical & mathematical aspects, limited mostly to "real optics." Stresses practical problem of maximum aberration permissible without affecting performance. All ordinary ray tracing methods; complete theory primary aberrations, enough higher aberration to design telescopes, low-powered microscopes, photographic equipment. Covers fundamental equations, extra-axial image points, transverse chromatic aberration, angular magnification, aplanatic optical systems, bending of lenses, oblique pencils, tolerances, secondary spectrum, spherical aberration (angular, longitudinal, transverse, zonal), thin lenses, dozens of similar topics. Index. Tables of functions of N. Over 150 diagrams. x + 518pp. 6⅛ x 9¼.   S366 Paperbound **$2.95**

SPACE-TIME-MATTER, Hermann Weyl. "The standard treatise on the general theory of relativity," (Nature), written by a world-renowned scientists, provides a deep clear discussion of the logical coherence of the general theory, with introduction to all the mathematical tools needed: Maxwell, analytical geometry, non-Euclidean geometry, tensor calculus, etc. Basis is classical space-time, before absorption of relativity. Partial contents: Euclidean space, mathematical form, metrical continuum, relativity of time and space, general theory. 15 diagrams. Bibliography. New preface for this edition. xviii + 330pp. 5⅜ x 8.   S267 Paperbound **$1.75**

RAYLEIGH'S PRINCIPLE AND ITS APPLICATION TO ENGINEERING, G. Temple & W. Bickley. Rayleigh's principle developed to provide upper and lower estimates of true value of fundamental period of a vibrating system, or condition of stability of elastic systems. Illustrative examples; rigorous proofs in special chapters. Partial contents: Energy method of discussing vibrations, stability. Perturbation theory, whirling of uniform shafts. Criteria of elastic stability. Application of energy method. Vibrating system. Proof, accuracy, successive approximations, application of Rayleigh's principle. Synthetic theorems. Numerical, graphical methods. Equilibrium configurations, Ritz's method. Bibliography. Index. 22 figures. ix + 156pp. 5⅜ x8.
                                    S307 Paperbound **$1.50**

PHYSICS, ENGINEERING

THEORY OF VIBRATIONS, N. W. McLachlan. Based on an exceptionally successful graduate course given at Brown University, this discusses linear systems having 1 degree of freedom, forced vibrations of simple linear systems, vibration of flexible strings, transverse vibrations of bars and tubes, transverse vibration of circular plate, sound waves of finite amplitude, etc. Index. 99 diagrams. 160pp. 5⅜ x 8.   S190 Paperbound **$1.35**

WAVE PROPAGATION IN PERIODIC STRUCTURES, L. Brillouin. A general method and application to different problems: pure physics, such as scattering of X-rays of crystals, thermal vibration in crystal lattices, electronic motion in metals; and also problems of electrical engineering. Partial contents: elastic waves in 1-dimensional lattices of point masses. Propagation of waves along 1-dimensional lattices. Energy flow. 2 dimensional, 3 dimensional lattices. Mathieu's equation. Matrices and propagation of waves along an electric line. Continuous electric lines. 131 illustrations. Bibliography. Index. xii + 253pp. 5⅜ x 8.   S34 Paperbound **$1.85**

THE ELECTROMAGNETIC FIELD, Max Mason & Warren Weaver. Used constantly by graduate engineers. Vector methods exclusively: detailed treatment of electrostatics, expansion methods, with tables converting any quantity into absolute electromagnetic, absolute electrostatic, practical units. Discrete charges, ponderable bodies, Maxwell field equations, etc. Introduction. Indexes. 416pp. 5⅜ x 8.   S185 Paperbound **$2.00**

APPLIED HYDRO- AND AEROMECHANICS by L. Prandtl and O. G. Tietjens. Presents, for the most part, methods which will be valuable to engineers. Covers flow in pipes, boundary layers, airfoil theory, entry conditions, turbulent flow in pipes and the boundary layer, determining drag from measurements of pressure and velocity, etc. "Will be welcomed by all students of aerodynamics," NATURE. Unabridged, unaltered. Index. 226 figures. 28 photographic plates illustrating flow patterns. xvi + 311pp. 5⅜ x 8.   S375 Paperbound **$1.85**

FUNDAMENTALS OF HYDRO- AND AEROMECHANICS by L. Prandtl and O. G. Tietjens. The well-known standard work based upon Prandtl's unique insights and including original contributions of Tietjens. Wherever possible, hydrodynamic theory is referred to practical considerations in hydraulics with the view of unifying theory and experience through fundamental laws. Presentation is exceedingly clear and, though primarily physical, proofs are rigorous and use vector analysis to a considerable extent. Translated by L. Rosenhead. 186 figures. Index. xvi + 270pp. 5⅜ x 8.   S374 Paperbound **$1.85**

DYNAMICS OF A SYSTEM OF RIGID BODIES (Advanced Section), E. J. Routh. Revised 6th edition of a classic reference aid. Much of its material remains unique. Partial contents: moving axes, relative motion, oscillations about equilibrium, motion. Motion of a body under no forces, any forces. Nature of motion given by linear equations and conditions of stability. Free, forced vibrations, constants of integration, calculus of finite differences, variations, procession and nutation, motion of the moon, motion of string, chain, membranes. 64 figures. 498pp. 5⅜ x 8.
                                    S229 Paperbound **$2.35**

MECHANICS OF THE GYROSCOPE, THE DYNAMICS OF ROTATION, R. F. Deimel, Professor of Mechanical Engineering at Stevens Institute of Technology. Elementary general treatment of dynamics of rotation, with special application of gyroscopic phenomena. No knowledge of vectors needed. Velocity of a moving curve, acceleration to a point, general equations of motion, gyroscopic horizon, free gyro, motion of discs, the dammed gyro, 103 similar topics. Exercises. 75 figures. 208pp. 5⅜ x 8.   S66 Paperbound **$1.65**

TABLES FOR THE DESIGN OF FACTORIAL EXPERIMENTS, Tosio Kitagawa and Michiwo Mitome.
An invaluable aid for all applied mathematicians, physicists, chemists and biologists, this book contains tables for the design of factorial experiments. It covers Latin squares and cubes, factorial design, fractional replication in factorial design, factorial designs with split-plot confounding, factorial designs confounded in quasi-Latin squares, lattice designs, balanced incomplete block designs, and Youden's squares. New revised corrected edition, with explanatory notes. vii + 253pp. 7 1/8 x 10. S437 Clothbound **$8.00**

NUMERICAL INTEGRATION OF DIFFERENTIAL EQUATIONS, Bennett, Milne & Bateman. Unabridged republication of original monograph prepared for National Research Council. New methods of integration of differential equations developed by 3 leading mathematicians: THE INTERPOLATIONAL POLYNOMIAL and SUCCESSIVE APPROXIMATIONS by A. A. Bennett; STEP-BY-STEP METHODS OF INTEGRATION by W. W. Milne; METHODS FOR PARTIAL DIFFERENTIAL EQUATIONS by H. Bateman. Methods for partial differential equations, transition from difference equations to differential equations, solution of differential equations to non-integral values of a parameter will interest mathematicians and physicists. 288 footnotes, mostly bibliographic; 235-item classified bibliography. 108pp. 5 3/8 x 8. S305 Paperbound **$1.35**

DESIGN AND USE OF INSTRUMENTS AND ACCURATE MECHANISM, T. N. Whitehead. For the instrument designer, engineer; how to combine necessary mathematical abstractions with independent observation of actual facts. Partial contents: instruments & their parts, theory of errors, systematic errors, probability, short period errors, erratic errors, design precision, kinematic semi-kinematic design, stiffness, planning of an instrument, human factor, etc. Index. 85 photos, diagrams. xii + 288pp. 5 3/8 x 8. S270 Paperbound **$1.95**

CHEMISTRY AND PHYSICAL CHEMISTRY

KINETIC THEORY OF LIQUIDS, J. Frenkel. Regarding the kinetic theory of liquids as a generalization and extension of the theory of solid bodies, this volume covers all types of arrangements of solids, thermal displacements of atoms, interstitial atoms and ions, orientational and rotational motion of molecules, and transition between states of matter. Mathematical theory is developed close to the physical subject matter. 216 bibliographical footnotes. 55 figures. xi + 485pp. 5 3/8 x 8.
S94 Clothbound **$3.95**
S95 Paperbound **$2.45**

THE PHASE RULE AND ITS APPLICATION, Alexander Findlay. Covering chemical phenomena of 1, 2, 3, 4, and multiple component systems, this "standard work on the subject" (NATURE, London), has been completely revised and brought up to date by A. N. Campbell and N. O. Smith. Brand new material has been added on such matters as binary, tertiary liquid equilibria, solid solutions in ternary systems, quinary systems of salts and water. Completely revised to triangular coordinates in ternary systems, clarified graphic representation, solid models, etc. 9th revised edition. Author, subject indexes. 236 figures. 506 footnotes, mostly bibliographic. xii + 494pp. 5 3/8 x 8. S92 Paperbound **$2.45**

DYNAMICAL THEORY OF GASES, James Jeans. Divided into mathematical and physical chapters for the convenience of those not expert in mathematics, this volume discusses the mathematical theory of gas in a steady state, thermodynamics, Boltzmann and Maxwell, kinetic theory, quantum theory, exponentials, etc. 4th enlarged edition, with new material on quantum theory, quantum dynamics, etc. Indexes. 28 figures. 444pp. 6 1/8 x 9 1/4. S136 Paperbound **$2.45**

POLAR MOLECULES, Pieter Debye. This work by Nobel laureate Debye offers a complete guide to fundamental electrostatic field relations, polarizability, molecular structure. Partial contents: electric intensity, displacement and force, polarization by orientation, molar polarization and molar refraction, halogen-hydrides, polar liquids, ionic saturation, dielectric constant, etc. Special chapter considers quantum theory. Indexed. 172pp. 5 3/8 x 8. S63 Clothbound **$3.50**
S64 Paperbound **$1.50**

TREATISE ON THERMODYNAMICS, Max Planck. Based on Planck's original papers this offers a uniform point of view for the entire field and has been used as an introduction for students who have studied elementary chemistry, physics, and calculus. Rejecting the earlier approaches of Helmholtz and Maxwell, the author makes no assumptions regarding the nature of heat, but begins with a few empirical facts, and from these deduces new physical and chemical laws. 3rd English edition of this standard text by a Nobel laureate. xvi + 297pp. 5 3/8 x 8.
S219 Paperbound **$1.75**

ATOMIC SPECTRA AND ATOMIC STRUCTURE, G. Herzberg. Excellent general survey for chemists, physicists specializing in other fields. Partial contents: simplest line spectra and elements of atomic theory, multiple structure of line spectra and electron spin, building-up principle and periodic system of elements, finer details of atomic spectra, hyperfine structure of spectral lines, some experimental results and applications. Bibliography of 159 items. 80 figures. 20 tables. Index. xiii + 257pp. 5 3/8 x 8. S115 Paperbound **$1.95**

EARTH SCIENCES

THE EVOLUTION OF THE IGNEOUS ROCKS, N. L. Bowen. Invaluable serious introduction applies techniques of physics and chemistry to explain igneous rocks diversity in terms of chemical composition and fractional crystallization. Discusses liquid immiscibility in silicate magmas, crystal sorting, liquid lines of descent, fractional resorption of complex minerals, petrogenesis, etc. Of prime importance to geologists & mining engineers, also to physicists, chemists working with high temperatures and pressures. "Most important," TIMES, London. 3 indexes. 263 bibliographic notes. 82 figures. xviii + 334pp. 5 3/8 x 8. S311 Paperbound **$1.8**

GEOGRAPHICAL ESSAYS, William Morris Davis. Modern geography & geomorphology rests on the fundamental work of this scientist. 26 famous essays presenting most important theories, field researches. Partial contents: Geographical Cycle, Plains of Marine and Subaerial Denudation, The Peneplain, Rivers and Valleys of Pennsylvania, Outline of Cape Cod, Sculpture of Mountains by Glaciers, etc. "Long the leader and guide," ECONOMIC GEOGRAPHY. "Part of the very texture of geography . . . models of clear thought," GEOGRAPHIC REVIEW. Index. 130 figures. vi + 777pp. 5⅜ x 8. S383 Paperbound **$2.95**

INTERNAL CONSTITUTION OF THE EARTH, edited by **Beno Gutenberg.** Completely revised, brought up-to-date, reset. Prepared for the National Research Council this is a complete & thorough coverage of such topics as earth origins, continent formation, nature & behavior of the earth's core, petrology of the crust, cooling forces in the core, seismic & earthquake material, gravity, elastic constants, strain characteristics and similar topics. "One is filled with admiration . . . a high standard . . there is no reader who will not learn something from this book," London, Edinburgh, Dublin, Philosophic Magazine. Largest bibliography in print: 1127 classified items. Indexes. Tables of constants. 43 diagrams. 439pp. 6⅛ x 9¼. S414 Paperbound **$2.45**

THE BIRTH AND DEVELOPMENT OF THE GEOLOGICAL SCIENCES, F. D. Adams. Most thorough history of the earth sciences ever written. Geological thought from earliest times to the end of the 19th century, covering over 300 early thinkers & systems: fossils & their explanation, vulcanists vs. neptunists, figured stones & paleontology, generation of stones, dozens of similar topics. 91 illustrations, including medieval, renaissance woodcuts, etc. Index. 632 footnotes, mostly bibliographical. 511pp. 5⅜ x 8. T5 Paperbound **$2.00**

HYDROLOGY, edited by **Oscar E. Meinzer.** Prepared for the National Research Council. Detailed complete reference library on precipitation, evaporation, snow, snow surveying, glaciers, lakes, infiltration, soil moisture, ground water, runoff, drought, physical changes produced by water, hydrology of limestone terranes, etc. Practical in application, especially valuable for engineers. 24 experts have created "the most up-to-date, most complete treatment of the subject," AM. ASSOC. OF PETROLEUM GEOLOGISTS. Bibliography. Index. 165 illustrations. xi + 712pp. 6⅛ x 9¼ S191 Paperbound **$2.95**

DE RE METALLICA, Georgius Agricola. 400-year old classic translated, annotated by former President Herbert Hoover. The first scientific study of mineralogy and mining, for over 200 years after its appearance in 1556, it was the standard treatise. 12 books, exhaustively annotated, discuss the history of mining, selection of sites, types of deposits, making pits, shafts, ventilating, pumps, crushing machinery; assaying, smelting, refining metals; also salt, alum, nitre, glass making. Definitive edition, with all 289 16th century woodcuts of the original. Bibliographical, historical introductions, bibliography, survey of ancient authors. Indexes. A fascinating book for anyone interested in art, history of science, geology, etc. DELUXE EDITION. 289 illustrations. 672pp. 6¾ x 10¾. Library cloth. S6 Clothbound **$10.00**

URANIUM PROSPECTING, H. L. Barnes. For immediate practical use, professional geologists considers uranium ores, geological occurrences, field conditions, all aspects of highly profitable occupation. Index. Bibliography. x +117pp. 5⅜ x 8. T309 Paperbound **$1.00**

BIOLOGICAL SCIENCES

THE BIOLOGY OF THE AMPHIBIA, G. K. Noble, Late Curator of Herpetology at the Am. Mus. of Nat. Hist. Probably the most used text on amphibia, unmatched in comprehensiveness, clarity, detail. 19 chapters plus 85-page supplement cover development; heredity; life history; adaptation; sex, integument, respiratory, circulatory, digestive, muscular, nervous systems; instinct, intelligence habits environment economic value, relationships, classification, etc. "Nothing comparable to it," C. H. Pope, Curator of Amphibia, Chicago Mus. of Nat. Hist. 1047 bibliographic references. 174 illustrations. 600pp. 5⅜ x 8. S206 Paperbound **$2.98**

THE BIOLOGY OF THE LABORATORY MOUSE, edited by **G. D. Snell.** 1st prepared in 1941 by the staff of the Roscoe B. Jackson Memorial laboratory, this is still the standard treatise on the mouse, assembling an enormous amount of material for which otherwise you would spend hours of research. Embryology, reproduction, histology, spontaneous neoplasms, gene & chromosomes mutations, genetics of spontaneous tumor formation, genetics of tumor formation, inbred, hybrid animals, parasites, infectious diseases, care & recording. Classified bibliography of 1122 items. 172 figures, including 128 photos. ix + 497pp. 6⅛ x 9¼. S248 Clothbound **$6.00**

BEHAVIOR AND SOCIAL LIFE OF THE HONEYBEE, Ronald Ribbands. Oustanding scientific study; a compendium of practically everything known about social life of the honeybee. Stresses behavior of individual bees in field, hive. Extends von Frisch's experiments on communication among bees. Covers perception of temperature, gravity, distance, vibration; sound production; glands; structural differences; wax production, temperature regulation; recognition communication; drifting, mating behavior, other highly interesting topics. Bibliography of 690 references. Indexes. 127 diagrams, graphs, sections of bee anatomy, fine photographs. 352pp. S410 Clothbound **$4.50**

ELEMENTS OF MATHEMATICAL BIOLOGY, A. J. Lotka. A pioneer classic, the first major attempt to apply modern mathematical techniques on a large scale to phenomena of biology, biochemistry, psychology, ecology, similar life sciences. Partial Contents: Statistical meaning of irreversibility; Evolution as redistribution; Equations of kinetics of evolving systems; Chemical, interspecies equilibrium; parameters of state; Energy transformers of nature, etc. Can be read with profit even by those having no advanced math; unsurpassed as study-reference. Formerly titled ELEMENTS OF PHYSICAL BIOLOGY. 72 figures. xxx + 460pp. 5⅜ x 8. S346 Paperbound **$2.45**

THE ORIGIN OF LIFE, A. I. Oparin. A classic of biology. This is the first modern statement of the theory of gradual evolution of life from nitrocarbon compounds. A brand-new evaluation of Oparin's theory in light of later research by Dr. S. Margulis, University of Nebraska. xxv + 270pp. 5⅜ x 8.   S213 Paperbound **$1.75**

THE TRAVELS OF WILLIAM BARTRAM, edited by **Mark Van Doren.** This famous source-book of American anthropology, natural history, geography is the record kept by Bartram in the 1770's, on travels through the wilderness of Florida, Georgia, the Carolinas. Containing accurate and beautiful descriptions of Indians, settlers, fauna, flora, it is one of the finest pieces of Americana ever written. Introduction by Mark Van Doren. 13 original illustrations. Index. 448pp. 5⅜ x 8.   T13 Paperbound **$2.00**

A SHORT HISTORY OF ANATOMY AND PHYSIOLOGY FROM THE GREEKS TO HARVEY, Charles Singer. Corrected edition of THE EVOLUTION OF ANATOMY, classic work tracing evolution of anatomy and physiology from prescientific times through Greek & Roman periods, Dark Ages, Renaissance, to age of Harvey and beginning of modern concepts. Centered on individuals, movements, periods that definitely advanced anatomical knowledge: Plato, Diocles, Aristotle, Theophrastus, Herophilus, Erasistratus, the Alexandrians, Galen, Mondino, da Vinci, Linacre, Harvey, others. Special section on Vesalius; Vesalian atlas of nudes, skeletons, muscle tabulae. Index of names. 20 plates, 270 extremely interesting illustrations of ancient, medieval, renaissance, oriental origin. xii + 209pp. 5⅜ x 8.   T389 Paperbound **$1.75**

NEW BOOKS

LES METHODES NOUVELLES DE LA MÉCANIQUE CÉLESTE by H. Poincaré. Complete text (in French) of one of Poincaré's most important works. Revolutionized celestial mechanics: first use of integral invariants, first major application of linear differential equations, study of periodic orbits, lunar motion and Jupiter's satellites, three body problem, and many other important topics. "Started a new era . . . so extremely modern that even today few have mastered his weapons," E. T. Bell. Three volumes; 1282pp. 6⅛ x 9¼.

Vol. 1. S401 Paperbound **$2.75**
Vol. 2. S402 Paperbound **$2.75**
Vol. 3. S403 Paperbound **$2.75**

APPLICATIONS OF TENSOR ANALYSIS by A. J. McConnell. (Formerly, APPLICATIONS OF THE ABSOLUTE DIFFERENTIAL CALCULUS). An excellent text for understanding the application of tensor methods to familiar subjects such as: dynamics, electricity, elasticity, and hydrodynamics. It explains the fundamental ideas and notation of tensor theory, the geometrical treatment of tensor algebra, the theory of differentiation of tensors, and includes a wealth of practice material. Bibliography. Index. 43 illustrations. 685 problems. xii + 381pp.

S373 Paperbound **$1.85**

BRIDGES AND THEIR BUILDERS, David B. Steinman and Sara Ruth Watson. Engineers, historians, and everyone who has ever been fascinated by great spans will find this book an endless source of information and interest. Dr. Steinman, the recent recipient of the Louis Levy Medal, is one of the great bridge architects and engineers of all time, and his analysis of the great bridges of all history is both authoritative and easily followed. Greek and Roman bridges, medieval bridges, oriental bridges, modern works such as the Brooklyn Bridge and the Golden Gate Bridge (and many others) are described in terms of history, constructional principles, artistry, and function. All in all this book is the most comprehensive and accurate semipopular history of bridges in print in English. New greatly revised enlarged edition. 23 photographs, 26 line drawings. Index. xvii + 401pp. 5⅜ x 8.   T431 Paperbound **$1.95**

MATHEMATICS IN ACTION, O. G. Sutton. Excellent middle-level exposition of application of advanced mathematics to the study of the universe. The author demonstrates how mathematics is applied in ballistics, theory of computing machines, waves and wavelike phenomena, theory of fluid flow, meterological problems, statistics, flight, and similar phenomena. No knowledge of advanced mathematics is necessary to follow the author's presentation. Differential equations, Fourier series, group concepts, eigen functions, Planck's constant, airfoil theory and similar topics are explained so clearly in everyday language that almost anyone can derive benefit from reading this book. 2nd edition. Index. 88 figures. viii + 236pp. 5⅜ x 8.

T450 Clothbound **$3.50**

MATHEMATICAL FOUNDATIONS OF INFORMATION THEORY by A. I. Khinchin. For the first time, mathematicians, statisticians, physicists, cyberneticists and communications engineers are offered a complete and exact introduction to this relatively young field. Entropy as a measure of a finite "scheme," applications to coding theory, study of sources, channels and codes, detailed proofs of both Shannon theorems for any ergodic source and any stationary channel with finite memory, and much more is covered. Bibliography. vii + 120pp. 5⅜ x 8.

S434 Paperbound **$1.35**

Write for free catalogues!

Indicate your field of interest. Dover publishes books on physics, earth sciences, mathematics, engineering, chemistry, astronomy, anthropology, biology, psychology, philosophy, religion history, literature, mathematical recreations, languages, crafts, gardening, art, graphic arts, etc.

**Available at your dealer or write Dover Publications, Inc.,
920 Broadway, Department TF1, New York 10, New York.**